THE
PERFECT
CORNER

THE
PERFECT
CORNER

A Driver's
STEP-BY-STEP GUIDE
to Finding Their
OWN OPTIMAL LINE
Through the
PHYSICS OF RACING

The Science of Speed Series

created by PARADIGM SHIFT DRIVER DEVELOPMENT
written by ADAM BROUILLARD

PARADIGM · SHIFT
DRIVER DEVELOPMENT

www.paradigmshiftracing.com

ISBN-10: 0-9973824-2-2
ISBN-13: 978-0-9973824-2-6

Published by Paradigm Shift Motorsport Books
The Perfect Corner and The Science of Speed
Series are trademarks of Paradigm Shift Driver
Development.

www.paradigmshiftracing.com

For information about custom editions, special
sales, premium and corporate purchases please
contact:

Paradigm Shift Driver Development
development@paradigmshiftracing.com
470.240.1582.

CONTENTS

"I don't want to believe, I want to know."

- Carl Sagan

THE PERFECT CORNER

Is there such a thing? The perfect corner, the perfect lap? Many drivers don't realize, but for a given car, setup, and conditions there is in fact a singular optimum way to navigate a racetrack in the minimum time possible. A set of fundamental physics based rules exist that can guide you in your never-ending pursuit of speed.

This quest to come ever closer to perfection is what drives many of us. This pursuit is one of the beauties of racing as the stopwatch always provides a measurable goal that you can always improve on. There is always that last second. That last 10th. That last 100th.

While a driver will never be able to achieve a truly perfect lap in reality, there is one place an actual perfect lap can exist. It can exist in the mind and give a driver a goal they can always strive to reach. That is what this book will introduce and explain. A set of rules that take a physics based approach to finding an optimal solution on track and distilling it into an intuitive way of driving that racers at any level can begin to apply.

We will take you through a fun thought experiment that will introduce the physics of racing and then learn to apply it as we optimize some real world corners. All with precise instructions and answers, but broken down so it's easy to understand. We will provide an exact method to find the optimum strategy all from the driver's eye point of view. No advanced vehicle dynamics knowledge is needed.

Understand though, that while the strategies we will learn to break down and analyze a track might be new, the actual driving techniques are not. We don't offer a secret new weapon that will have you smashing track records by next weekend. Although they may not all have understood exactly why they drove the way they did, many of the top drivers in the world have been driving by the principles that we teach for decades. You can find old videos of champion drivers like Senna, Schumacher, and others driving laps that reflect these methods. We actually recommend reviewing videos of world-class drivers as you work through this book. Try to identify how what you are learning is reflected in the videos of their top performances.

So we don't offer an instant path to the top podium step. A good bit of car control training will be required for that. But one thing you can develop quickly is knowledge. The knowledge to never be confused about what you should be doing on track. The knowledge to know exactly where you are losing time, and what those champion drivers are doing that makes them faster. You will no longer have to rely on trial and error. You will no longer have to try to mimic the laps of faster drivers. Instead, you will be able to watch their laps and identify where **they** are losing time. You will have a solid goal to focus on as you reach ever closer toward perfection. Learning this new method will require a commitment from you however, because it will probably be a true paradigm shift in the way you will look at a racetrack from now on. For many novice drivers with little previous knowledge this should be easier, but for veterans, you may have to set aside previously held assumptions.

PAR · A · DIGM SHIFT

NOUN

A FUNDAMENTAL CHANGE IN APPROACH OR UNDERLYING ASSUMPTIONS.

LINE THEORY

When a novice first gets into motorsport they will often be taught a basic racing line and then instructed to steadily increase their speed. This is a good approach as it is generally a safe way to learn and will eventually produce some respectable lap times.

> Line Theory is the term we use for the set of rules you will use to optimize your path.

At a certain point however, this student will usually hit a wall. They just can't go any faster and they can't figure out why. Many will then turn to data and video and look at laps of the faster drivers to try to figure out what the differences are. They will try to emulate what the faster drivers are doing and through trial and error and lots of work their lap times will slowly start to creep lower again. After years and years of driving different tracks and cars, they will build up a mental database of what to do at each corner and in each situation.

But there are a lucky few who seem to be able to almost bypass this process entirely. They just have a natural instinct for what it takes to go around a track quickly. Whether they realize it or not, they are following the basic principles of physics that produce lower lap times. Just like the gifted child that knows instinctively how to move their body to put the maximum power behind a ball being kicked or thrown, these drivers seem to have an innate grasp of the fundamentals that create a champion driver.

They can quickly move beyond a basic learned racing line and actually create an ideal one as they drive. While learning a basic racing line can take you quite a way, if you wish to reach your ultimate potential you'll need to go beyond the basics and learn the rules that created that line in the first place.

What makes a certain path the fastest way around a track? Why do we want to use the whole track? Why do we sometimes not? What is so special about slow-in, fast-out? In short, what are those champion drivers doing that makes them so darn fast, lap after lap?

While this ability only comes naturally to a select few, luckily it can be learned by just about anyone and it doesn't require a PhD in physics either. Everything the driver needs to know is actually fairly simple and can be broken down into a set of fundamental rules. We call these fundamental rules Line Theory.

We say these drivers are creating a line as they drive because there is actually no such thing as a correct line. Only the correct line at this exact moment and it will change based on where exactly your car is right now and how it responds at the limit. There is no reason to worry about trying to learn an ideal line until you are driving at your limit, because what happens at the limit is actually creating your line.

We will teach you instead to focus on the limits of the track and then use Line Theory rules to constantly optimize your driver inputs based on these track limits. Because of this, you will need to start thinking of the line more as a result than a path to follow. Every small variance and mistake will change how you optimize the rest of the corner at every instant. We'll see how all you are really doing is constantly correcting mistakes during a corner. Ideally, very small mistakes.

Therefore, while Line Theory rules will never change, your ability to control the car will cause the resulting line to change. As your car control skills improve and evolve, so will your optimal line. Even if you have excellent car control skills though, there will always be at least some variations that change how you will optimize a corner each time. The resulting line and the driver inputs used will never be exactly the same even if they only change by the smallest of margins.

THE LIMITS OF CONTROL

In this last section, we mentioned that your optimal resulting line would change as your car control abilities change. Because of this, it's important to understand that Line Theory and car control need to be considered completely separate.

The primary reason is that the ideal path you take will always be limited by your ability to control the vehicle. Although the rules will be the same, a novice driver will have a different resulting optimal line than an advanced driver. A quick example is that a more advanced driver will be able to control a car closer to the limit and would be able to turn more and achieve a higher speed by the point they put the power down for corner exit. This will require a different optimal apex than a novice driver.

> No matter what your skill level, you can still apply the fundamentals of Line Theory to improve your lap times.

There are a lot of Line Theory fundamentals packed into that example we haven't explained yet, but the take home point is that no matter what your skill level, you can still apply the rules of Line Theory to improve your lap times.

It's also important to understand that unless specified otherwise, we are always discussing the situation as if the driver is controlling the vehicle at the limit as best they can. One rule of Line Theory is that under normal circumstances, for ultimate lap time performance, there is never a time that you are not trying to use the vehicle's potential to its maximum. As a novice advances in their car control skills, that potential will change and thus their resulting line will change. How they apply Line Theory fundamentals will always however, stay the same.

It's also vital that you don't make the mistake of confusing failures in car control for failures in Line Theory. The differences we are talking about are sometimes only fractions of a second and most of the time a non-optimal technique done perfectly is going to be faster than an optimal technique done poorly. Drivers with superior car control abilities can make all sorts of non-optimal approaches work if they are only going up against drivers of lesser skill.

What's most important is that you understand **why** a technique is faster even if you haven't developed the car control abilities to do it properly yet. Line Theory is not a list of techniques to try out and see if they work for you and to discard if you are not immediately faster. Doing so shows a lack of understanding of what Line Theory represents. Line Theory is just the term we use for the application of the basic principles of physics on a racetrack. These principles are immutable until the physics of our universe decide to change.

Therefore, the most powerful aspect of Line Theory is not that it's just a list of rules that tells you the fastest way around a track, but once you have a complete understanding, you will **know** the fastest way. Wouldn't it be great if you could never have to worry about trying other lines, techniques, etc... because you know what you are doing is correct? It's a very powerful feeling to remove all doubt from your driving and know exactly why you were slow or why you were fast. Learning Line Theory will remove that doubt forever, and from then on, the only thing holding you back will be how far you can push the limits of your control.

VEHICLE DYNAMICS SIMPLIFIED

While there is certainly a lot of vehicle dynamics theory going on behind the scenes in this book, from the driver's perspective there is really very little you need to know once you are in the car. The only thing you really need to understand at this point to work through this book is that cars have an overall traction circle.

For those who are unfamiliar, a traction circle represents the concept that a car generates grip (or force) in all directions fairly equally. While each tire also has a traction circle and is generating a force, if you combine all those tire forces, you have an overall force acting on the car's center of gravity.

We use a circle because the maximum force attainable is fairly even in all directions. If you try to push a parked car from various sides, it will take roughly the same amount of force to get it sliding.

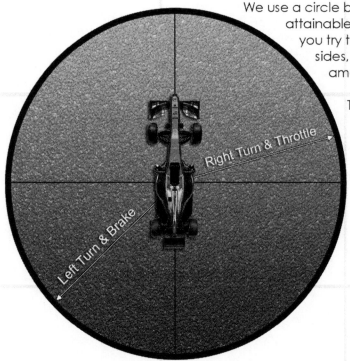

Right Turn & Throttle

Left Turn & Brake

This same concept applies at speed and although there is a vast multitude of variables affecting the exact grip available at any instant, really all you need to know right now is the basic idea that it's similar in many different directions.

For example, a given car might either brake with 1 g of force or turn with 1 g of force or a combination of braking and turning that generates 1 g of force in a diagonal direction. Very few cars will be able to actually accelerate with the same force that they can brake or turn, but we'll get to that later.

Also realize that the traction circle is not just a pretty representation. You could actually imagine a jet thruster coming from the center of gravity pushing the car in the direction of the arrow. The tire forces will combine to create a net force on the car and this force will modify the car's path.

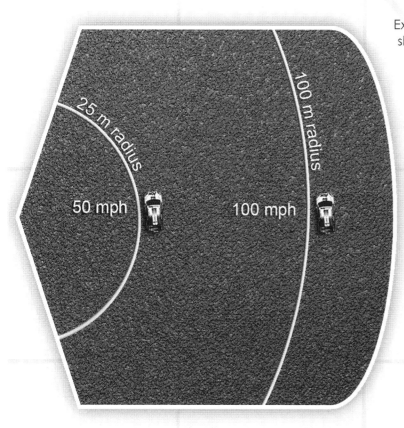

Expanding this concept, you should also understand that for any given radius a car travels on, it could only achieve a certain maximum speed. This basically means that if you drive a bigger circle, you can drive faster before the car is no longer able to maintain its arc. This should be fairly intuitive, but a quick example is that if a given car can drive at the limit around a 100 m radius circle at 100 mph, on a 25 m radius circle it would only be able to drive 50 mph before sliding wide.

Grip vs speed is an exponential relationship and this example ignores aero effects, but that is not important right now. Just that you understand the general concept that a bigger circle allows a faster speed at the limit.

The forces discussed in this book are ultimately generated at the tire/track interaction.

This is pretty easy to understand when you have big changes in radius and speed, but realize this also holds true for small changes. Racecars will almost never be on a constant radius arc. They will normally either be increasing or decreasing their radius. As this radius changes, the attainable speed will also change. Even if the radius only changes by 1 cm, the attainable speed will also change. This is true with all cars including those with high downforce. A smaller radius will always require a lower speed and vice-versa. There is no free speed or grip, and you can't cheat the laws of physics.

ASTRONAUT RACING

Before we get into learning about how to drive the perfect corner on a racetrack, we find it useful to take a step back and look at the basic physics involved from an intuitive standpoint. A car, it turns out, is actually quite complicated, as you have to worry about silly things like steering, throttle, brakes, tires, and so on. Let's take all of that out of the equation and take a fun little detour... in space!

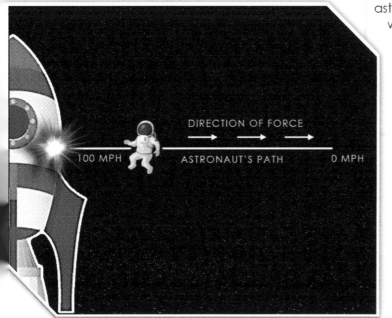

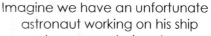

DIRECTION OF FORCE

100 MPH   ASTRONAUT'S PATH   0 MPH

Imagine we have an unfortunate astronaut working on his ship when an explosion damages his suit and launches him into space at 100 mph directly away from the ship. Because his suit was damaged he needs to get back to the ship as **quickly as possible,** but his only source of propulsion is the fire extinguisher that he brought with him on his spacewalk for some reason. The fire extinguisher will let him generate maximum thrust in any direction virtually instantly. He just has to point it and pull the trigger.

Our astronaut quickly surmises that to get back to the hatch as quickly as possible he will simply point the extinguisher away from the ship and blast away to bring him back to the ship in the minimum possible time. This will cause his 100 mph initial velocity to slow to zero and then he will begin to gain speed on the way back to the hatch. Let's ignore the hazardous side effect right now that he would enter the ship at 100 mph.

This simple thought experiment tells us two very important things right off the bat. The first is that to minimize his time to get back he wants to use the absolute maximum thrust he possibly can directly away from the ship for the entire flight. Our illustrations for this section will use arrows to depict the direction he is pointing his extinguisher. You'll see why this is important as we continue.

Secondly, if we plotted his speed vs time on a graph it will be a V shape with his speed starting at 100, then dropping to 0 and going back up to 100. The more force he can generate, the more angled the V shape and the lower his time in space. His minimum speed is also at the furthest point from the ship. Before moving on, make sure you understand the astronaut's actions because, believe it or not, what he just did is the very core of Line Theory.

INTRODUCING TURNS

Now let's start changing the scenario so we can see how this simple concept can be expanded. On his next mission, the very unlucky astronaut is working on the tail of his new ship at the other end from the entry hatch. There is an explosion yet again and he must get back to safety as quickly as possible. To reach his goal he's going to have to stop his outward motion and reverse it as well as move to the side in the direction of the hatch. We are going to assume he needs to enter the hatch straight on or he crashes into the side and explodes. This assumption will help to simplify this thought experiment.

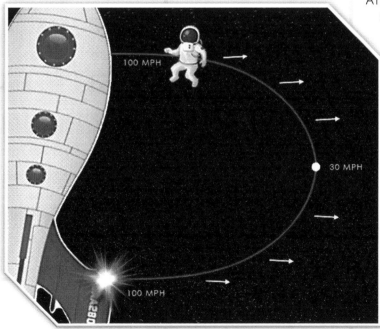

After being launched into space, the astronaut, using his advanced physics knowledge, quickly points the extinguisher away from the ship but partially angled downward in the illustration to decelerate his movement away from the ship, but also start moving him laterally toward his goal. His speed will slow and once he's reached the farthest point away from the ship, he starts to accelerate back toward it.

At his farthest point, he needs to change the angle of the extinguisher to the other side so his path will slowly straighten and he'll arrive at the airlock dead on. The astronaut's actions cause his path through space to be in the shape of a parabola. Well-informed readers might recognize this as the basic shape of a racing line through a 180-degree corner. He decelerates to a minimum speed at the farthest point from the ship (the apex in racing terms) and then accelerates back toward it.

If he aimed his extinguisher perfectly in the proper direction, he just optimized his path to the hatch and it's impossible for him to get there any faster than this. The illustration shows his minimum speed as 30 mph, but the actual speed doesn't matter right now. What matters is that you understand that it's the minimum speed he will achieve. If you placed a floating cone out at the point he reaches his minimum speed, he would have also optimized his path around this obstacle as if it were a corner on a track.

It's not so much the shape of the path, but the direction of force that is important right now. The shape of the path is simply the result of that force. His extinguisher is always basically going to be blasting in the same direction opposite the ship. He does need to angle the extinguisher sideways to start and stop the sideways movement, but this is a relatively shallow angle and the majority of the force he feels is going to be his deceleration and then acceleration toward his ship. If you plotted his path using a speed vs time graph you would again see a V shape. The bottom of the V would be his minimum speed of 30 mph.

If you are having a hard time grasping why this one singular direction of force is so important to minimize the astronaut's travel time, try to imagine what would happen if he pointed his extinguisher in any other direction or didn't use maximum thrust. What would that do to his travel path and time in space? Some people are better at visualizing this than others, but it's very important to have an intuitive understanding of what we are explaining here so it's definitely worth the time to do your own thought experiments if necessary.

Before moving on we also wanted to point out that while the astronaut must angle his extinguisher to create the sideways movement, a car will also always have a similar sideways force generated while turning. Not to get ahead of ourselves here, but since a car can basically only generate force with its engine while going forward, it needs to do some rotating to be able to do that at corner exit. This needed rotation will require at least some sideways force.

We don't want to overcomplicate this example, but did want to point out what that sideways angle of the astronaut's extinguisher related to in car terms. It's actually a driver's goal to minimize this sideways force by only using the bare minimum needed to move the car over to the apex. Any extra speed carried past the apex than is necessary just has to be reversed during corner exit. In a car, this will cause a driver to be unable to use as much throttle as would be optimal and this hurts their exit.

Minimizing these sideways forces leaves as much force as possible to be used in the primary direction. Throughout this book when we speak about the "ideal direction" we are referring to the direction that you are currently trying to accelerate in as quickly as possible by generating the maximum force attainable. Understand though, that there will always be some sideways force needed as well.

CHANGES IN FORCE DIRECTION

So now we understand that optimizing the direction of force is the key to the astronaut's salvation. So far these forces have basically always been going in the same direction, but let's now look at what happens when we change things up a bit to look more like a 90 degree turn on a racetrack and see how this affects our forces needed.

On his third mission, our astronaut starts to suspect that maybe he should seek a different career as he is blasted into space yet again. This time however, his ship is damaged beyond repair and he must make it to the sister ship. Unfortunately, there is also a piece of space debris in the way that he must first navigate around.

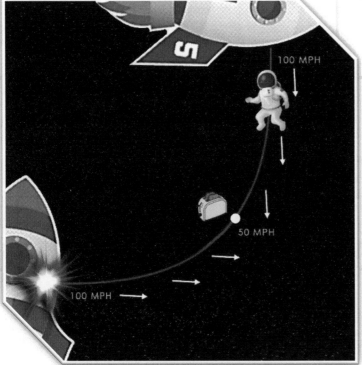

The astronaut again using his great understanding of physics looks at the obstruction and quickly calculates that he needs to immediately blast his extinguisher at a slight outward angle to slow him down from 100 mph and reach the corner of the obstruction at the proper speed. For this example, we made that speed 50 mph, but again, the actual speed is not important right now, just that you realize it's the slowest speed he attains on his trip. Also note that because the starting speed is the same as in the previous example, the needed direction of the extinguisher and the resulting shape of the path up to this apex is exactly the same as the beginning part of the previous path. You could overlay them and they would match up exactly. We will look at the reasons for this more in-depth in the corner entry section.

Immediately as he passes the obstruction he turns his extinguisher to start moving him toward his goal in the minimum overall time possible. To keep this example simple the explosion launched the astronaut at the exact speed he would need to optimize this corner, but later we'll see how this optimal starting speed is determined. An analogous situation in a car for the explosion would be the point a driver decides to start turning their car during straight-line braking.

> The better a driver can generate and direct these forces with their vehicle the lower their lap times will be.

Again, we can see the shape of the astronaut's path, but also more importantly it shows the direction of force he is generating with the extinguisher. The key difference from the previous example is that once past the obstacle, the optimum direction of force changes. To travel in the minimum time possible around an obstacle, or in racing terms an apex, you want to generate as much force as possible pushing you backwards as you decelerate and turn toward the obstacle (apex) and then after you pass the obstacle you want to generate as much force as possible pushing you toward your final goal.

The direction of force needing to be generated simply follows the angle of the corner. If you moved the sister ship, the forces needed after the apex would follow it. If you changed the point where the astronaut started, the direction of forces needed prior to the apex would simply follow that as well. On a racetrack, this ideal direction will basically just follow the same angle as the track does at corner entry and exit.

It might be confusing to think if you are trying to get to the other ship in the shortest time possible that you would start out by trying to push yourself in a completely different direction. But remember, the astronaut starts his path going 100 mph already. If he does not immediately start slowing down and turning, he will fly past the apex out away from his goal and have to spend extra time coming back toward it.

It's important to understand this section and it might be worth rereading a few times and taking the time to think about it if necessary. While driving a racecar, it's very important to have a constant awareness of where the ideal direction is that you are trying to maximize acceleration. In the real world, the better a driver can generate and direct these forces with their vehicle to accomplish this, the lower their lap times will be and that's really at the heart of what this book is about and ultimately the core goal of Line Theory.

Of course, just telling a driver to go "generate some forces" doesn't really do much good on its own. As usual, the devil is in the details, but to understand the basic physics at work is helpful when trying to get an intuitive understanding of what you are really trying to accomplish on track. When trying to work through this book or trying to work up a particularly tricky section of track, it might be helpful to think back to this section. If you ever find yourself confused, just ask yourself, "What would the astronaut do?"

BACK ON EARTH

Okay, now we are well on our way to becoming a professional astronaut racer, but how does this help us down here on Earth where drivers need to worry about silly things like steering wheels and gravity. As it turns out, a car can actually mimic the actions of our astronaut quite well. While the astronaut just points his extinguisher and blasts away, a racecar driver would need to use his steering, brakes, and throttle to generate these same forces with the tires.

It's important to realize that the forces we talk about are ultimately generated at the tire/track interaction. For example, during corner exit, it's not really the engine that's generating the needed force, but the engine's ability to rotate the wheels in combination with the driver turning the steering wheel that generates the force from the tires. The driver not only has control over the total amount of force, but can also alter which way the forces are directed. The better a driver can maximize and direct these forces to mimic the actions of the astronaut the faster they will be able to complete a corner.

Let's work through this step by step as we learn what we are trying to accomplish in each section of a corner.

CORNER EXIT

It's always a debate whether to teach corner entry or corner exit first. It's natural to want to go in order, but we really can't go any further before first developing an understanding of what we are trying to achieve at corner exit and how everything revolves around the apex.

For our first example, let's look at the hairpin at Suzuka. Remembering that for any given radius, there is a maximum speed we can achieve, we'll put a car through the turn that on the limit can drive in a perfect circle at 50 mph. The white line represents the path of the car, but the shaded circle shows how the path of the car during the corner is completely circular.

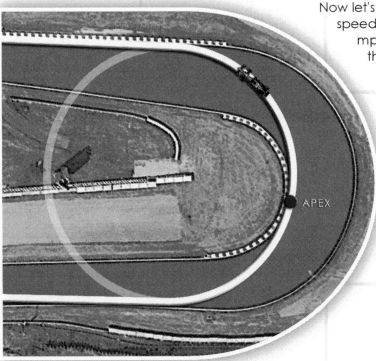

Now let's drive the hairpin with a speed limiter in the car set to 50 mph so you just floor the throttle and drive a perfect circle along this line. We are still at the limit of traction of the tires; we just do not have any extra power to accelerate. This circular path causes the apex to be pretty close to the middle of the corner.

Take note that in this corner exit section we are going to be driving the beginning half of the corner in a perfect circle so we can more easily visualize the differences in speeds and angles at different apexes. This would require the driver held a basically constant steering wheel position and speed from corner entry to the apex. The car is still at the limit of traction though. As you'll see later, this is not the way you should optimally drive corner entry, but it helps with explanation and simplicity for now. A circular entry is also much easier from a car control standpoint so for a more novice driver it's not a bad approach as you improve your skills.

With the speed limiter on, there is no way to exit this corner any faster as we are generating the absolute maximum forward thrust possible. There is also no way to go faster at the apex by driving a bigger circle and still stay on track at corner exit unless you lifted off the throttle. This line is the optimum corner exit for the car right now.

While this circular corner exit would be optimized for a car driving with a speed limiter on, being able to apply more power at corner exit would get us to our goal faster and lower lap times. That should be fairly intuitive, but to understand exactly why from a physics standpoint let's look at what is happening from the viewpoint of our astronaut.

To illustrate this we've added arrows representing the direction of forces the car is generating with its tires. Just like in space, the arrows should be pushing the car in basically one ideal direction that follows the angle of the track at corner exit. As you can see at the apex, the arrows are going in the proper direction pushing the car toward its goal, but as it progresses through the remainder of the corner exit, they progressively start pointing in a non-optimal direction away from the desired direction of travel. Only once the corner is fully complete would the force move back in the proper direction.

IDEAL DIRECTION

The final small arrow is shown to indicate the force pushing the car down the straightaway after the cornering is complete. Because of the limited power, it is a much smaller arrow than the others. Remember, we were driving the entire corner on the limit of traction, but as soon as the cornering is over the tires are no longer required to generate very much grip in comparison. Again, from a physics standpoint, the forces being generated are always from the tire/track interaction. Only a powerful engine would bring the tires near their limit once on the straightaway.

Now let's remove the limiter and see if we can do better. Remember though, we were already on the limit of traction, so even with more power, if we try and drive along the same line as previously, but accelerate at any point we will run wide and start heading off track. In fact, if we even try to use one tiny extra bit of power than what we used earlier we will run off track at the exit. Therefore, in order to use this extra power we must turn more before we begin accelerating. This changes our apex in two ways. It moves it further in the corner (a later apex), and we will arrive at the apex at a slower speed.

A LATE(R) APEX

It's important to understand that there is no such thing as a "late apex" or an "early apex." There is only a correct apex, which can be either later or earlier in the corner than it was before. If we overlay a smaller circle going from the edge of the track at corner entry to the inside, you can see why you will arrive at a later apex slower. Remember, the smaller a circle that a car drives on, the slower the speed it will be able to attain. The exact speed is not important right now, just that you realize it's slower than the earlier apex because the circle is smaller. The later an apex is the smaller the circle and the lower the apex speed.

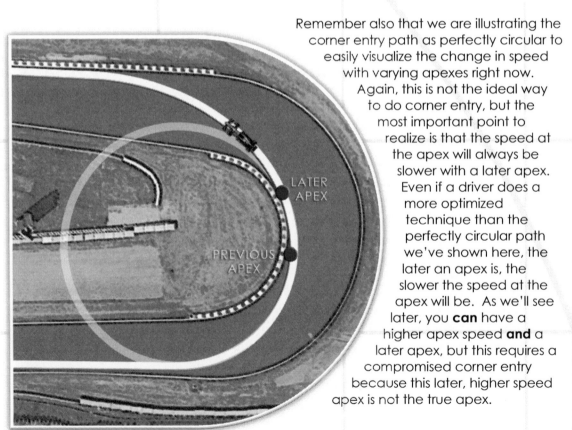

Remember also that we are illustrating the corner entry path as perfectly circular to easily visualize the change in speed with varying apexes right now. Again, this is not the ideal way to do corner entry, but the most important point to realize is that the speed at the apex will always be slower with a later apex. Even if a driver does a more optimized technique than the perfectly circular path we've shown here, the later an apex is, the slower the speed at the apex will be. As we'll see later, you **can** have a higher apex speed **and** a later apex, but this requires a compromised corner entry because this later, higher speed apex is not the true apex.

This figure shows the two previous examples laid on top of each other. Look closely at how the differing size circles representing different speeds possible will hit the apex at different places and angles. Now try to visualize for yourself how different size circles representing different apex speeds will meet up with the corner at different points and angles. The smaller, slower circles will always create an apex further in the corner. Conversely, a larger, faster circle will always hit it earlier. This will create a steady progression of speed and angle as the apex moves along the inside of the track.

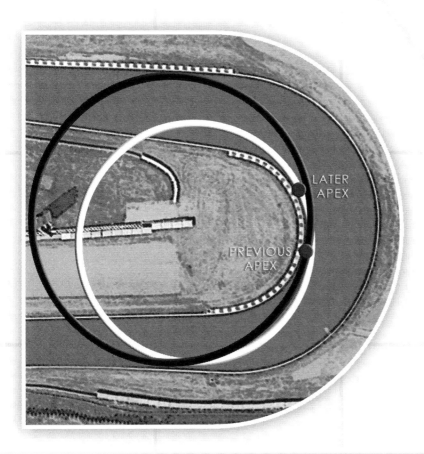

CORNER EXIT POWER APPLICATION

All right, so to use more power we need to turn more and be at a greater angle and therefore be going slower at the apex. Well how much power do we want to use? The basic answer is **all of it**, but technically what we are trying to achieve is the maximum force the tires can provide to accelerate us in the ideal direction.

In many lower-powered cars, this is basically going straight to full throttle in all but the slowest corners. In a high-powered car or slippery conditions, you might be only using partial throttle throughout the entire exit. In a car with lots of aero downforce, you might be increasing power as you gain grip with increased speed.

> On every standard corner, on every track in the entire world your goal is to achieve maximum acceleration as quickly as possible at the apex.

The goal is always the same though. Maximum acceleration, which is either full throttle if you are at the edge of understeer or the maximum throttle possible that keeps you from going into excessive wheelspin. It's not technically the wheelspin that is important, but that is a good shortcut that works for many cars. An example of where this shortcut doesn't work is with off-road driving where maximum acceleration is achieved with high amounts of wheelspin. The goal is still maximum acceleration, but they achieve this in a different way.

It's also not just forward acceleration we are talking about here, it's combined vector acceleration. The total combination of lateral and longitudinal force throughout corner exit. This introduces the concept of acceleration arcs, which we'll look at later in the book. For now though, just remember that you are trying to achieve maximum acceleration in the ideal direction just like the astronaut.

Okay, so we know we want to use as much power as possible, but when do we begin using this power? You might have heard before that you shouldn't get on the throttle until you are sure you won't have to lift. This is almost always true, but it's even simpler than that. The ideal acceleration point, every single time, is **at the apex**. That's right. On every standard corner, on every track in the entire world your goal is to achieve maximum acceleration as quickly as possible at the apex. Not before, not after. **AT THE APEX**. You can see we think this is important to remember.

You actually use your ability to achieve maximum acceleration from the apex to find where the apex should be. If maximum acceleration from the apex out does not allow you to just barely stay on track at corner exit it simply means you made a mistake and need to adjust your apex until you find one that lets you do that.

Let's go through some examples so we can see how this works. Going back to our high-powered car in the Suzuka hairpin, we just crossed our original centrally located apex and then accelerate as hard as possible. We've removed the speed limiter now so wheelspin would be no problem to achieve if we wanted to. The car starts to rocket toward the track edge and we need to lift so we don't run wide.

Okay that was wrong. Let's move the apex further around the corner so we can turn more before we begin accelerating. Now this time, as we have traveled on a much smaller circle we are almost all the way through the corner and have a much later apex before we accelerate. Because we had to drive a smaller circle, we have also arrived at the apex slower. Now we are able to use more power which is a step in the right direction, but it actually felt really easy to stay on track so that's not right either. Let's pick somewhere between our first two tries. Now the placement of our apex as well as our apex speed and angle is in between the previous two.

We'll come back to this in a moment to see what happens, but you can probably see a pattern beginning to develop here. Your proper apex is always going to be determined by the current acceleration potential of your car. The faster a car can accelerate in a given corner, the later the apex needs to be. When people talk about "momentum cars" what they really should say is that you need a relatively earlier (and higher speed) apex than if the car had more acceleration potential in that corner. Even a Formula 1 car in a very high-speed corner might look like it's driving like a "momentum car" with a relatively early apex. At the other end of the spectrum, a low powered car in a very tight corner would have good acceleration potential and so would need a relatively later apex.

It's actually a common misconception that the length of the straightaway following a corner is a deciding factor on your apex. This is actually not true, as you will see coming up. If there is a 1-mile straight or a 1-meter straight, you use the same rules to optimize your corner exit.

> As you pass the apex, the only reason you should not be at full throttle is to avoid excessive wheelspin.

As you pass the apex, the only reason you should **not** be at full throttle is to avoid excessive wheelspin because this reduces the forces the tires can generate. Typically excessive wheelspin is detected because it will cause oversteer. Wheelspin doesn't always cause oversteer in every car, but when it does, your throttle use shouldn't be limited until you reach true power oversteer where a steering correction cannot compensate and only a reduction in throttle keeps the rear in check.

Conversely, if you experience understeer and run off track you don't need less throttle, you need a later apex. To put this another way, if you are ever understeering during corner exit, you had better also be at full throttle. If that carries you off track, you need a later apex, not less throttle because less throttle will reduce the maximum tire force produced. The ideal solution is instead changing the apex to redirect that maximum force. Just remember if you ever find yourself going wide or not using the whole track, this doesn't change how much throttle you use, it only changes your ideal apex.

This is an important Line Theory rule to remember, but why exactly is it true? Let's look at the situation again from a basic physics standpoint. This figure shows our new later apex, but more importantly the direction of forces that the tires are generating. As you can see these now mimic the forces that our astronaut created and they are pushing the car in the ideal direction.

The greater acceleration potential a car has for a given corner, the closer to the ideal direction its tire forces can push it during corner exit and the later of an apex it will need to do that. This later apex must be at a higher angle and a lower speed than if the car had less acceleration potential in that corner.

But what happens when a car doesn't have very much acceleration potential in a corner? This could simply be a car with very little power compared to its level of grip or it could be such a fast corner that the car isn't able to accelerate very much even at full throttle.

The resulting forces would look like this previous figure showing non-optimal force generation. This is simply just a case of "as good as it gets." While later in the corner the forces generated are not directed optimally, the total **net force** created through the corner exit is the best the car can do. If you attempted to apex later like a more powerful car, the engine simply wouldn't have the power to bring the tires near their limit. So although you could aim the forces better, the overall net amount would be lower and the result would be slower than possible. Not just lower corner exit speed, but more time spent in the corner as well.

IDEAL DIRECTION

THE PERFECT APEX

Just remember, you always want to maximize the acceleration of the car using as much track as possible during corner exit because that will always give you the best net result of tire forces.

To bring this full circle let's continue with our previous Suzuka hairpin example. Back in our more powerful car, we cross our new apex and get hard on the throttle as we drive at the absolute limit with all four tires giving everything they can. The outside of the track comes rushing up and the outside wheels just clip the edge as we rocket down the straight. "That was good," we say to ourselves. And it was. We just optimized this corner exit and found our perfect apex. The perfect apex for right now anyway.

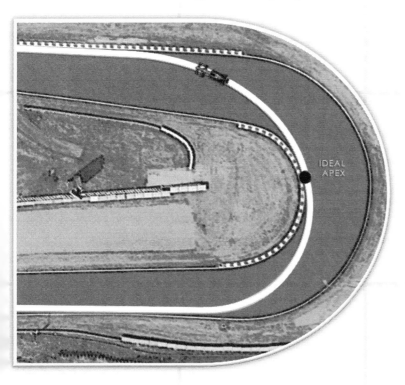

IDEAL
APEX

APEX ANGLE

It's important to understand that it's not really a certain point in the corner that signifies the apex. It's actually the angle that the car is facing, or more accurately, the direction it is currently traveling that really matters. For example, imagine if you have a cone on an autocross course as the center of a hairpin turn and a car needs to go down around the cone and back. Any car driving this corner will have its apex point be right at the cone, but depending on the apex speed needed for a proper corner exit, the angle their car is traveling while passing the cone will be different.

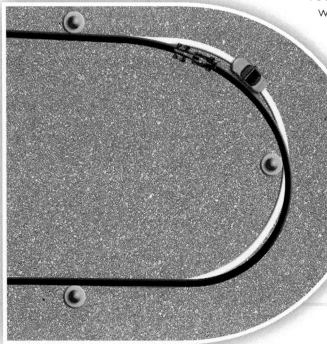

This figure shows two different apexes. You can see that although both cars would hit the apex at almost exactly the same place the more powerful dark line car that needs a later apex would be at more of an angle as it passed the cone.

When using Line Theory principles on track to identify your apex on shorter corners it's normally more important to pay attention to not so much where an apex is in a corner, but what direction the car is traveling as you reach the apex.

At the opposite end of the spectrum, there will be big, long corners where it might be easier to remember the apex as a point on the track you hit rather than the angle. It's still the angle that actually signifies the apex, but using the point it meets up with the track might be easier to remember. Try to visualize how differing size circles representing different apex speeds laid over various shape corners will change the angle and point where they create an apex.

Another way to look at the apex is that it is the point on the inside of the corner that most compromises your ability to go faster through that corner. Starting from the center of the track, if you continuously drive a faster and faster line you will eventually start to hit some point on the inside of the corner. **That** is now your apex and everything then becomes about optimizing around that point. As you optimize your line, this point might change some as your new optimized apex angle could change where it hits the inside of the track.

Also realize that while the apex is usually some point on the inside curbing of a road course corner, or a cone on an autocross course, it can be anything. It just has to be a point that most limits your speed. It could be the edge of a slick spot while racing in the rain. It could be a deep rut or big bump when driving in dirt. It could be a small kitchen appliance blocking your way. It could even be an imaginary point out in the middle of the track if you've made a mistake and missed your braking point.

Just remember your acceleration and deceleration always revolves around this one point and angle that is most limiting you right now.

THE MYTH OF THE SUPER-LATE APEX

Wait, wait, wait. But if our goal is to maximize our corner exit speed why don't we just start accelerating before the apex and then we will be going even faster than if we wait until the apex to start accelerating? Just search for "late apex" on the internet and you will find countless examples of websites and images depicting this idea. Even many of the most popular racing books and schools advocate accelerating prior to the apex.

While you **can** actually increase your apex speed and initial straightway speed this way, it will result in an overall greater elapsed time. Not just for the lap, but also for the corner. The reason is that normally you gain only a few mph at corner exit, and as we have learned in order to do this, you have to drive a tighter radius at the beginning of the corner (a smaller circle). This means an even slower minimum speed and most importantly more time spent turning the car.

It's this last bit that is key. You often hear you want to get on the throttle as soon as possible to minimize lap times. This is absolutely true, but the key is that it should be based on **time**, not distance. From the point that you hit the brakes to enter the corner, you want to minimize the **time** before you are able to get back to maximum acceleration and you do this by changing the direction the car is traveling as quickly as possible at corner entry.

It turns out the fastest way to accomplish this puts your acceleration point **at the apex.** Remember how the astronaut always reached their slowest speed at the apex. The force generated by the extinguisher decelerating the astronaut before the apex was the equivalent of a car trail braking, and the extinguisher force after the slowest point is the equivalent of applying power at corner exit. We are just using the car to mimic what the astronaut was doing.

When you start acceleration before the apex, you are actually optimizing the corner for a false apex out in the middle of the track somewhere. Basically driving as if you are going around an obstacle that is not really there. To fully understand this we will need to work through the corner entry section coming up soon, but let's look at it briefly right now.

This figure shows an optimized apex as well as the super-late apex. They both still have a circular entry path though. If you do a super-late apex and begin accelerating early, you might have a speed of 52 mph at the point you hit the inside of the track, whereas the optimum apex would have an apex speed of only 50 mph. But at the same point in **time** that the super-late apex car hits that 52 mph apex, the optimum apex car is 10 meters further down the track and is already going 53 mph. Their ideal acceleration arcs will match from the point they were both at 52 mph and so the optimum apex wins every time. We'll talk much more about acceleration arcs later on.

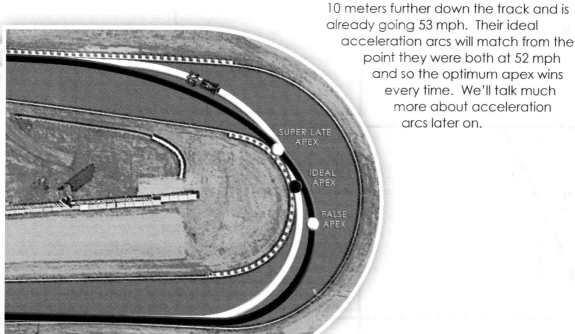

SUPER LATE APEX

IDEAL APEX

FALSE APEX

So the problems with the super-late apex is actually related more to corner entry than exit. You'll see how the problems with the super-late apex are even greater once we start driving an optimized corner entry.

Truthfully, you do actually use this early acceleration technique sometimes because it can gain you straightaway speed that can be used in certain circumstances. This could be on the last corner of a lap to maximize speed as you cross the start line on a qualifying run or to setup a pass during a race. But from a current lap time perspective, it is **always** slower than optimal because you are taking longer than necessary to turn the car and begin accelerating.

Spec Racer Ford is one of the largest amateur racing classes in the US featuring low-cost, identically prepared cars that rewards driving skill over budget.

CORNER EXIT CHEAT SHEET

Before we move on to corner entry, let's recap the standard corner rules we have learned so far:

- The apex is always the optimum point to begin maximum acceleration, although this doesn't necessarily mean full throttle.
- The apex is defined by the direction the center of gravity of the car is traveling as it passes by.
- Different apex speeds and the resulting angle can make the car pass the inside of the track (create an apex) at different points depending on corner shape.
- A slower, higher angle apex will always hit the inside of the track later, and a faster, lower angle apex will hit it earlier.
- The apex should be the point of minimum speed and turn radius achieved during the corner.
- A car with greater acceleration potential in a corner will need a relatively later apex than if the car has less acceleration potential in that corner.
- The ideal apex will require the car to use the entire width of the track at corner exit. This produces the greatest possible total net force pushing the vehicle in the ideal direction.
- The ideal direction follows the same angle as the track does at corner exit.

Once you've established how to identify an ideal apex, your goal is then to turn the car to that angle of travel as fast as you can. It's this necessity of turning that brings us to corner entry and our overriding goal there, which is, in simple terms, to get the car turned as quickly as possible. Done properly this will cause the car to pass the apex at the perfect angle and speed that produces an ideal corner exit.

It might seem that the highest apex speed achievable that still allows a perfect corner exit might be ideal. But we're about to see how the perfect speed is actually not the highest one achievable. You can have two identical drivers in two identical cars that both have a perfect corner exit, but the one with the higher apex speed will actually complete the corner slower and have a worse lap time. We'll see how this all comes down to the way the car is turned during corner entry.

It's important to understand that when we say turn, we mean to actually change the car's direction of travel, not just rotate the car. After all, you can pull on the handbrake to initiate a quick rotation, but you haven't actually changed the car's direction of travel much. It's very important to understand the difference. If it's hard to grasp this, think about the astronaut. He uses his extinguisher to change his direction in space (or turn), but it actually doesn't matter which way he is facing (rotation) as he does it.

For the rules of Line Theory, it's not rotation that matters, but the actual changing of the direction that you are traveling, or again simply turning. It's this necessity to turn that brings us to the importance of the Euler spiral.

SPIRALING INTO CONTROL

Since we strive for an intuitive approach, this is as advanced as the physics and math are going to get in this book. Looking at the spiral, really all you need to know is that as the line progresses it continuously bends more and more. Technically speaking, the radius decreases as the line length increases. Engineers that lay out train track designs use portions of Euler spirals to smoothly transition trains along the tracks so there is no sudden increase in g-force. The spiral continues into infinity, but we are really only concerned with the first 90 degrees of it.

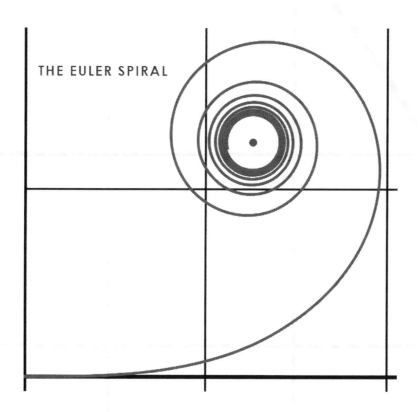

THE EULER SPIRAL

This figure shows the beginning of the Euler spiral as well as lines that show the starting angle and where the spiral hits 90 degrees. So how does this relate to driving a car? Any time you tighten the steering in a car it can be represented by a portion of the Euler spiral as the radius the car is traveling on is becoming smaller.

Beyond simply showing what happens to the path of the car when you turn the wheel, the shape of the Euler spiral also represents the absolute fastest way you can change direction by combining deceleration with steering. You might think that if you want to change the direction of the car as quickly as possible, you would just want to use steering, but this is actually not the case. The reason comes back again to the direction of force the tires create.

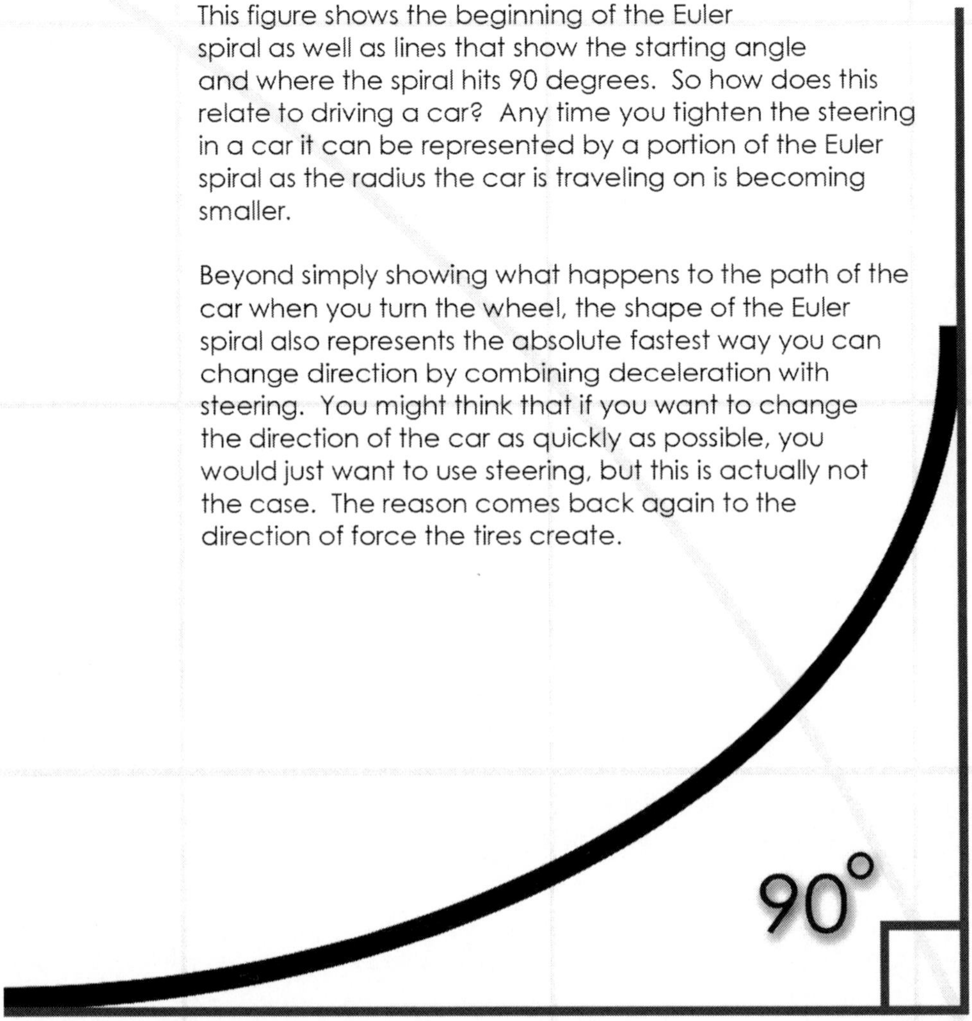

90°

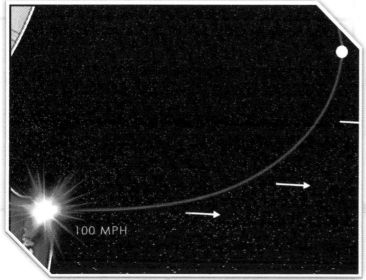

100 MPH

Thinking back again to our astronaut, you might notice that the path he is taking up to the furthest point from the ship is the first 90 degrees of an Euler spiral. Remember also, as he blasts away with his extinguisher most all of the forces created are going in one direction. As he alters his path as quickly as possible, he will be tracing the exact shape of an Euler spiral. It's the direction of force that creates this path shape in the case of the astronaut and when driving a car.

Because of this, the most important feature of the Euler spiral for us is that the radius is constantly decreasing. Creating as much force as we can in this optimum direction causes this to happen as quickly as possible. The starting speed and force applied will change the overall size of the spiral, but the basic shape will always remain the same. If the force applied was instead progressively aimed more toward the bottom of the illustration, you would steadily have more of a circular path, and the rate of turning would be slower. If you tilted the extinguisher toward the top more, you would have a path that started out with a slower rate of turning at the beginning and then became faster at the end, but only because your speed is slower than ideal.

The bottom line is that to continuously decrease the radius of your path (turn) as quickly as possible, you want to generate the maximum force you can in the optimal direction and the path this creates will be in the shape of the spiral.

The corner exit also has no influence on the direction of force needed at corner entry. The ideal direction will always be basically backwards from the initial direction from which the spiral started. The apex simply dictates at what point you stop traveling on the spiral path and corner exit begins. The more radius change the corner requires, the more of the Euler spiral you use.

Look again here at the astronaut illustration of the 90-degree corner. The corner entry up to the apex is exactly the same shape and has the same direction of needed force as with the 180-degree corner because the goal is exactly the same. Reduce radius (turn) as quickly as possible. In these two examples, because the starting speed and force created was the same you could actually lay them on top of each other and the corner entry paths would line up perfectly.

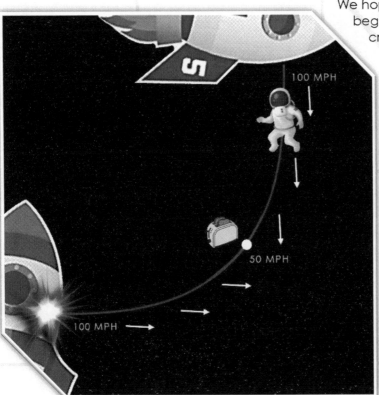

We hope that you are beginning to understand that creating as much force in the optimum direction is a common concept, so how can we best mimic this with a car at corner entry? Starting with maximum braking, a driver progressively releases the brakes as they turn the steering wheel. More experienced readers might recognize this as trail braking. While in concept this is quite simple, the execution can take years to master.

Many people understand that trail braking is a key to finding speed and know it deals with combining braking and steering, but fundamentally why is trail braking and driving a spiral shaped entry a good thing? From a physics standpoint, why does it actually make you faster and lower lap times?

> Changing direction as quickly as possible to the angle that allows maximum acceleration gives us the optimum path through a corner.

To find out why, we just need to combine what we have already learned. When a driver uses steering and brakes together they can not only maximize the total amount of force the tires produce, but also direct that force. If the driver is able to direct and maximize that force properly, they will travel on the path of an Euler spiral. This spiral shaped path is the absolute fastest way they can get the car to change its **direction** of travel. Also remember from the corner exit section that the key characteristic of the apex is not where it is, but the **direction** the car is traveling in as it reaches that point. It's this apex angle that is limiting when we are able to achieve maximum acceleration, which produces the lowest elapsed time for the remainder of the corner.

Bringing these principles together gives us the rule that represents the core of Line Theory. **Changing direction as quickly as possible to the angle that allows maximum acceleration gives us the optimum path through a corner.**

We like laying out rules like this, but unless you really understand what it means from a driver's perspective on track, it's not much use. We find one of the best ways to begin to understand what we are really trying to accomplish here is just to work through some real world examples.

THE EULER SPIRAL ON TRACK

Turn 11 at Laguna Seca is a great corner for this first example. It's more than 90 degrees, but far from 180. You will be going fast enough in most any car where straight line threshold braking will be required. Let's just go ahead and lay our spiral down at corner entry and see what it tells us.

We've put a gradient on the spiral so you can more easily visualize the change in speed as the car slows down. The beginning of the spiral meets up with the end of our straight line braking and is the part at which the driver decides to start changing direction. We try to avoid the word turn-in because it rather implies a quick movement of the steering wheel. As you can see with the spiral, the radius change is gradual so it will start with primarily braking and not much steering.

As you progress along the spiral, for any given point, you are at a certain angle and there will be a certain speed attainable at that exact point. If driven optimally, the speed you enter the spiral will determine the size of the spiral, but it will basically always be the same shape. This gives us our first variable at corner entry.

DIFFERENT SPEEDS, DIFFERENT SIZES

This illustration shows the path of a car doing two different entry speeds for its spiral, but starting from the same point at the grey line. The dark path represents a spiral entry speed of 60 mph and the white path would be a spiral entry speed of 50 mph. It's important to note that for a given exit speed from the previous corner this would require different braking points. The vertical black and white lines show where the different braking points would be for these different spiral-starting speeds.

In both of these spirals the driver is trying to get the car turned as quickly as possible, but when starting from the slower speed he is able to do that a good bit faster and reach the apex. So the slower, white spiral must be correct then right?

BRAKING
POINTS

SPIRAL
START

60 mph
50 mph

Not necessarily and we'll see why in a moment, but first we want to point out that the important takeaway from this example is that although the dark spiral is a good bit larger than the white, it is exactly the same shape. Driven optimally, spiral entry speed will affect the size of a spiral, but not its shape. More technically speaking the radius is decreasing faster on the white spiral than the dark, but the rate of change is always going to be pretty linear in both cases.

Another important takeaway here is to understand the influence a driver's abilities have on the spiral's size. Remember the spiral simply represents the fastest change of direction achievable. If a driver is able to get the car to do this quicker, their spiral will be smaller. For example, if that was a novice driver who drove the darker line starting at 60 mph, an expert driver in the same car might be able to stay on the white line starting from 60 mph because they were able to get the car to slow down and turn faster. This shows how novice and expert drivers will have different optimal lines because of how their different spirals will create different speeds at the apex. This change in speed requires a different apex and a different corner exit.

> Novice and expert drivers will have different optimal lines and apexes because of how their different spirals will create different speeds at the apex.

A novice driver is also more likely to have bigger variations in how quickly they can reduce their radius. Errors could cause a driver to momentarily travel on a circular path or even increase their radius. For this section though, we are assuming we have a driver of set skill level where if they want to have a different size spiral they need to start from a different speed.

Okay, so what is the use of the larger dark spiral if it's just going to send you off track? This time let's now bring the starting point of the dark spiral back so that its path will meet the apex. You can't see the braking points in this illustration, but the dark spiral braking point will now be really close to the white spiral braking point. For a given spiral entry speed you will create a certain size spiral and you then move your starting point so that your path will meet the apex. Every different spiral entry speed and therefore size will have a certain spot it must start from in order to hit the apex. Any later and you will miss the apex and any earlier will send you off the inside of the track.

Okay, so now the dark spiral is still sending us off track, but at least its starting point is correct. The black and white vertical lines show where the spirals are starting and now both are hitting the apex. Note that these are still exactly the same spirals from the previous example, but now starting from the proper points, we can see their effect on how the car will

arrive at the apex. The larger dark spiral will hit the apex at a higher speed and less of an angle than the white spiral. In short, an earlier apex. Conversely, a later starting and slower spiral will always give you a slower apex speed and a higher angle. In other words, a later apex. The dark spiral is still excessively early here, but we wanted the differences to be easily visible in the illustrations. There is actually a fairly small range of apexes that will be useable.

SPIRAL START

60 mph
50 mph

To recap, the Line Theory rule we are learning here is that the spiral starting speed will affect the overall size of the spiral, and then you adjust your spiral starting point and ultimately braking point so your path meets the apex. This will allow you to reach the apex in the minimum time possible while also allowing you to adjust the speed and angle you pass the apex until you find the optimum.

We'll get back to how to determine this optimum apex shortly as it's really what all this has been leading up to, but first we should give a little disclaimer before you start trying to use graphics programs to find the ideal line on a racetrack.

Sim racing can provide everything from a safe, low-cost introduction to motorsport, to an advanced training tool for professional drivers.

NOT ALL SPIRALS ARE CREATED EQUAL

The example spiral we've been using here for illustration is very linear in that the radius decreases at a fairly constant rate along the line. In reality, even driven optimally by an expert driver, every car and track situation will have an influence on the exact shape the spiral takes. This is because the maximum grip that a car generates with its tires is not always exactly the same. A certain car may have more or less grip in various directions or at different speeds. There could be track banking or numerous other variables affecting the exact shape.

While in general these are going to be fairly small variations, what it will do is squish or stretch the spiral. If you have a fairly normal car on a flat track that can slow down at the same level of grip that it corners it will have a traditional Euler spiral shape with basically a linear change in radius. However, let's say you have a car with a lot of downforce that steadily loses grip as it slows down. It will stretch out the spiral. The driver is still attempting to get the car to turn as quickly as possible, but the result will look a little different.

On the opposite end of the spectrum would be something like a rear-brake-only kart. It can generate a lot more force in cornering than it can in braking so the spiral will be squished into a more circular shape. It won't be perfectly circular though, even a kart with no brakes at all would not have a completely circular entry, as there would still be induced drag from the tires slowing it down. Only a vehicle with a partially stuck throttle that exactly counteracted all the drag forces would have a perfectly circular entry.

This is why it's important to understand that the spiral simply represents a driver's corner entry goal of changing direction as quickly as possible. While this usually results in a classic Euler spiral shape, a driver shouldn't feel like they messed up if their line doesn't match up exactly. Remember, the line is simply a result of following the proper rules. It is not a path they are attempting to follow. During corner entry, as long as they are decreasing the radius of the path they are on as quickly as possible, they are achieving their goal. No matter the car or situation, the quicker the driver is able to get the car to do that, the better.

Autocross is a one-car-at-a-time event where everyone from average Joes in daily drivers to serious competitors in full-blown racecars compete for the fastest time through a racetrack made entirely of traffic cones.

OPTIMIZING CORNER ENTRY

Now that we understand more about the Euler spiral, how do we match it with our optimum apex so we know where it should begin? In remembering back to the corner exit section we know that we want to pass the apex with the optimal speed and angle that allows maximum acceleration, but will just barely keep us on track during corner exit.

The more acceleration potential a car has for a given corner, the later and slower you are going to initiate your spiral as that way you will hit the apex at the higher angle and lower speed that you need for a proper corner exit.

Let's look at a few ways we can mess this up so we can figure out how to do it correctly. For these first examples, we'll use a perfect circle as our corner exit marked by when the line turns white to make everything easier to visualize. This represents when the car would go to full acceleration, which would basically be full throttle here. This circular exit would be caused by a car with high grip in comparison to its horsepower and so therefore very little acceleration potential in the corner. Many entry class racecars have corner exits that look just like this.

MISSED BRAKING POINT = MISSED APEX

Just to make sure we are clear, no matter when you start your spiral, if you miss the apex, your braking point was just too late. This leads to too fast of a spiral entry speed no matter where you decide to start turning. You actually have to be able to hit the apex before you can begin to figure out what your apex angle should be.

It might be easiest to think of where you start turning as your ability to adjust the angle you hit the apex and then you might need to adjust your braking point to make sure you are able to actually hit that apex. How much this changes your braking point depends on the shape of the inside of the corner. Remember, different apex angles will sometimes hit the inside of the track at different points.

You might be wondering what would happen if the driver in this example continued slowing down and turning in the spiral to get closer to the apex? If the driver were to do this, they would hit the apex way too slow and late for a good corner exit and actually make their mistake even worse. This illustration actually shows how to make the best of a missed braking point as the corner exit is still optimized the best it can be based on the botched entry.

BRAKING AND SPIRAL TOO EARLY

Conversely, if you are able to run off the inside of the track, your braking point and spiral is too early. Remember, once you initiate your spiral the goal is to turn the car as quickly possible and therefore its path will be that of an Euler spiral. You aren't driving a "line" in the shape of the spiral. That shape is just the result of your goal, which is to turn as quickly as possible. In this case, with too slow and small of a spiral you would end up driving off the inside of the track.

Clearly, you wouldn't want to actually do this, and a correction would be needed during corner entry. This correction would compromise both the corner exit speed and the elapsed time through the corner, but the earlier you made this correction, the less the penalty would be.

REACHED APEX – MISSED EXIT

Okay so we are doing a bit better now. We've hit our apex, but there is a problem. We just can't keep the car on track at corner exit without having to lift at some point. We hit the apex going too fast and too early. So what does that tell us? Start the spiral later and slower.

THE PERFECT CORNER

Terrific! This time with the correct spiral starting point and speed, we hit the apex at the exact speed and angle needed to allow an ideal maximum-acceleration corner exit where we just barely stayed on track. This is the absolute fastest way this driver, in this car, can negotiate the corner.

Time for a bonus round. This figure shows what happens when we give the car twice the power so it will need a later apex to optimally use that power at corner exit. As we've learned, this requires a later and slower apex and so therefore a later and slower starting spiral.

This gives us another Line Theory rule. The more acceleration potential a car has for a given corner, the later and slower you are going to initiate your spiral as that way you will hit the apex at the higher angle and lower speed that you need for a proper corner exit. This works exactly the same way as in our corner exit section, but now we have an optimized corner entry as well.

Remember again though, all of this talk of spirals, accelerating from the apex, and how they work together is just a way to visualize and explain how this will look on track. It's just a shortcut for the basic physics. All we are really doing here is directing and maximizing the ideal forces needed. Go back and reread the astronaut section and try to use your newfound knowledge of corner optimization to understand how it compares to what the astronaut was doing.

It's also fun to try to see how Line Theory applies to different activities in the real world that might not have at first seemed applicable. Watch videos of short-track speed skating and watch how a skater's movements change at corner entry up to the apex where they are grip and not power limited. Notice how this changes in long-track skating where they are always power limited and never grip limited. From a Line Theory standpoint, this means that in long-track there actually are no turns that need optimized. It's just an exercise in maximizing power and reducing drag.

Try watching a horse race as well. Are the horses ever grip limited and would need to follow the principles of Line Theory? How would things change if there were tight corners and the horses needed to slow down? For your answer, look up barrel racing. See if you can find other examples where Line Theory might apply.

We sincerely hope you are now starting to get a grasp of a driver's true goal in a corner. What might seem overly complicated at first actually becomes quite simple once you are able to see how a basic understanding of the effect a force has on an object's movement is being used in Line Theory to optimize your driving. Sometimes though, a great way to learn what you should be doing is to look at some examples of what you shouldn't.

THE "ARTIST RENDITION" LINE

This is an example of what we like to call an "artist rendition" line. We've overlaid it on a shaded version of our previous optimum line so you can easily see the difference. You can find variations of this example on the internet and unfortunately in many popular books. We wanted to put it here as a warning that just because you can draw a line on a track map or drive a certain line at a slower speed doesn't mean it's feasible or even possible at race speeds.

So what is the big problem with this line? At first glance, it looks really good. It's shorter than our optimum and has very straight lines so must be faster during corner entry and exit. Must be better right? The problem comes back again to what our Euler spiral represents which is the fastest way to change direction. Remember again, the spiral progressively changes its radius as the line continues. If you look at this line right around the apex, you suddenly have a very fast radius change, which would only be possible if the car was not using all of its available grip in the first part of the corner. This would require a significant change in force as the car turned. You can't cheat the laws of physics and while there will be variations in grip that will create slight alterations in the shape of your spiral; you can never have sudden big changes in your rate of turning if the car is driven at the limit.

CIRCULAR ENTRY

For a non-optimal, but at least realistic approach, let's now look at the traditional circular entry as depicted in our corner exit section. This circular entry path is what many more traditional drivers do and we actually recommend for beginning drivers to start with more of a circular entry and slowly work their way into the spiral. Primarily because, from a car control standpoint, it is much easier. You are basically just driving as you would around a skid pad. Trail braking properly is a good bit harder. In addition, as you'll see, the circular entry can lead to an even slightly better corner exit speed than the spiral, which can be used in certain circumstances.

Overall lap times will of course be slower however so it should always be a driver's goal to push themselves into optimizing their corner entry by using trail braking and the spiral. For now though, let's just compare the two.

Here is an illustration of an optimized spiral entry overlaid with a circular entry. As we learned earlier, for any given radius that we are traveling, there is a maximum speed we can attain.

It always depends on the capabilities of the car and driver, but let's just say the point at the apex for our optimized entry represents 50 mph and is the maximum apex speed we can attain and still make the corner exit with maximum acceleration. It might be hard to tell from the illustration, but the radius of our circular entry technique is actually slightly larger than the radius of the spiral at the apex. That means that if they had the exact same apex angle our perfect circle entry probably would be in the 52-53 mph range or so. Well, that's faster so that must be a better way to drive correct? Well, no, and the reason is two-fold.

First off, we've already determined the maximum speed at our current apex is 50 mph if we want to be able to maximize

acceleration and stay on track at corner exit. That means the circular entry car, going slightly faster there, would not be able to accelerate from the same point, and would actually need a slightly later apex and a slower apex speed for a proper corner exit.

The perfect circle car actually **can** still achieve a faster apex speed than the spiral in this way by maybe one or two mph, but it's still slower overall and that's because of our second primary reason, which we hope you have figured out by now. While the Euler spiral car has been decelerating all the way up to the apex, the perfect circle car has been traveling at 51 mph since the very beginning point where it turned in for the corner. So not only is the path the circular entry car traveling longer, but it is also done at a lower average speed and will require an earlier braking point.

It should be fairly intuitive to understand that this is slower, but let's look at it from a physics standpoint by adding some arrows in to represent the direction of forces the tires are generating.

In comparison to the Euler spiral, if you turn the car along a constant arc, the forces are going to start out going sideways and will only finally start going close to the proper direction at the apex. The astronaut would not be very pleased.

Even if driven at the limit, the result is that you travel at a lower average speed and take a longer path, which together equates to a greater elapsed time. So we can see now that although the circular path may be easier from a car control standpoint and it has its pluses, it's ultimately slower.

Before we move on to our next corner entry technique we need to cover a problem we've introduced here as its resolution is primarily the reason the Euler spiral and not any other method of corner entry is fastest. Did you spot the problem?

THE INFINITE STRAIGHTAWAY PROBLEM

We've learned that with the circular entry you have a faster apex speed and corner exit speed than with the spiral. Even if the circular entry was only 1 mph faster and took much longer to get there, if you have a long enough straightaway and a constant 1 mph advantage you would catch up to the spiral entry and pass it eventually right? We mentioned earlier that the length of the straightaway has no effect on your cornering technique so how can we resolve this seeming conflict?

This problem was introduced because in our desire to teach this in the simplest way possible we used a corner exit that is not completely realistic. For simplicity, with the perfectly circular corner exit in our examples, your apex speed will always exactly be your corner exit speed. This is theoretically possible for a given car if the drag exactly matched the power generated, but it would only work for one exact speed. While very little acceleration and a relatively circular path is actually very close to what happens in reality for many lower-powered cars, every car is always going to have a specific acceleration rate it can achieve for a given corner. It's never going to be a constant arc at every speed. This is because every car's corner exit will always be limited by its ability to turn while achieving maximum acceleration. The acceleration rate and arc will change based on grip levels available, but for any given car, corner, and condition it will always be the same.

Let's run through an example so we can understand what we are talking about here. Imagine you have a car accelerating from a standstill while also turning left as much as possible with any of its remaining grip. If driven optimally it will follow the same exact arc every time if the conditions are the same. This is essentially what corner exit is. Using maximum acceleration and then turning with any available remaining grip.

Now take that same car and start it from 50 mph doing the same thing. If you overlay the arcs starting from where they both are going 50 mph, the paths will match exactly if all other conditions are the same. This is because in both cases at 50 mph the car will have the same power applied at the tires and the same grip levels, which in turn will allow the same steered angle, and therefore the exact same path.

> It doesn't matter who is going faster at the point they reach the straightaway. The only thing that matters is who started accelerating first.

Understanding this principle now, let's take it back to our problem. We first have the spiral entry that will hit 50 at the apex and start its acceleration arc. We then have the circular entry that will hit the apex at 51 and start its acceleration arc, but it takes longer to get to that apex. **If the spiral entry car reaches 51 mph before the circular entry car starts accelerating from 51 at its apex then the spiral car wins.** This is because their acceleration rates and arcs will match from that point on and whoever is in front wins.

Based on our knowledge of how optimized the forces are in these different corner entries, we know the spiral wins every time. Remember, every technique should be judged on how well it can create and direct the desired optimal forces, because that is ultimately what determines the fastest way through a corner. The winner is always going to be the one who can best mimic the astronaut.

So again, it doesn't matter who is going faster at the point they reach the straightaway. The only thing that matters is who started accelerating first. Remember, you want to start accelerating as quickly as possible based on time, not distance, because time is what matters on a racetrack. This shows that whether you have no straight at all or one a mile long, the spiral wins every time. It also shows that the traditional method of checking your speedometer at corner exit to see how you did in the corner doesn't work. While it might give you a ballpark idea, the exact speed you reach at a certain **point** on track is meaningless. What really matters is how soon in **time** you can reach that speed from the point you hit the brakes.

You might be wondering what would happen if the other car had a ten mph advantage and not just a one mph advantage over the Euler spiral car. Well this is actually impossible unless you compromised your corner entry even more by doing a super-late apex. Imagine an exaggerated version where the car would drive 100 meters past the apex and then come flying back at the corner at top speed. Clearly, it would have a faster apex, corner exit, and straightaway speed, but also clearly, it would be a much slower way to complete the corner. Many times doing a thought experiment with a highly exaggerated version of something can help you understand it better.

THE ACCELERATION ARC

Before continuing on to our next non-optimal entry technique, let's look a little more at this concept of an acceleration arc. If you look back at our astronaut's acceleration arc, it exactly matches his entry spiral. This is because he is always generating the exact same amount of force in all directions so his path will have a very linear change in radius.

Cars however, do not have equal force generating capabilities in all directions. During corner entry, most cars generate grip pretty equally in cornering and braking because they normally have the braking power to lock up all four tires. Because of this, they generate basically the same grip under braking as they do in cornering as well as any combination of those.

LOWER-POWERED CAR ARC
PERFECT EULER SPIRAL ARC
DRAG RACING CAR ARC

However, during corner exit, even a high-powered car that could easily produce wheelspin will not accelerate as well as it corners if it is only driving the rear wheels. During straight-line acceleration, basically only the rear tires are providing any force because the front tires are not really doing anything at that point. A high-powered car that can corner at 1.0 g might only be able to accelerate at 0.7 g. A front-wheel drive car will be even worse under acceleration.

This change in force will cause the acceleration arc to be more circular shaped than an Euler spiral. Even a Formula 1 car that gains a lot of downforce as it accelerates still does not quite have the grip under acceleration to create an ideal Euler spiral shape. In addition, in cars with high downforce, this shape will change based on speed. As the speed in a Formula 1 car gets faster, the cornering grip grows as the acceleration potential shrinks. The acceleration arc becomes more and more circular and it starts to drive like a "momentum car" in very fast corners.

In order for a car to actually have an exact Euler spiral shaped corner exit you would need the same acceleration force potential as cornering force potential. This would require 4-wheel drive and enough power to keep all tires at the edge of wheelspin through the entire exit. The only kind of car that would actually stretch out the spiral would be something like a drag racing car that had poor cornering performance and was only built for straight-line acceleration.

We hope you can see now why the circular corner exit we have used as an example is actually quite realistic for many cars. While high-powered cars can get fairly close to an Euler spiral shape, lower-powered cars have a more circular acceleration arc. A low-powered car might corner at 1.2 g, but only accelerate forward at 0.2 g at race speeds. For comparison, if you wanted to make the same arc shape at corner entry that this low-powered car creates at corner exit you would need a car that had no brakes and was only using induced tire drag to slow down.

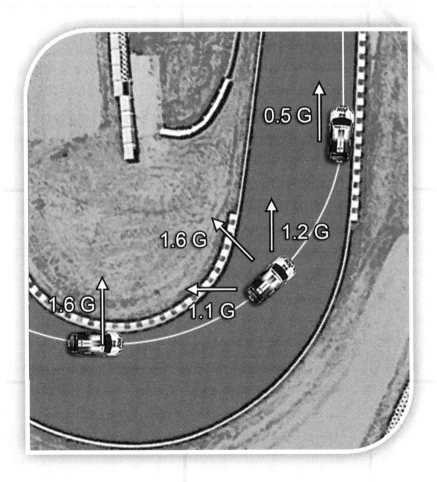

We want to make sure you understand the arc shape is not caused by a sudden change in force when the car hits the straightaway though. It is caused by a change in the direction of force throughout the corner exit and the resulting change in speed that creates.

A car that accelerates straight at 0.5 g and corners at 1.6 g might be generating around 1.2 g of force halfway through the corner exit pushing it in the ideal direction. It would still be at the limit and pulling close to 1.6 g though. It would just lack the engine power to push that force in a more optimal direction. 1.1 g of that total force would be used to keep the car from going off track. The direction the 1.6 g of force the car produced at the limit would steadily shift as the car progressed through the exit and become less and less optimal. If you are wondering how 1.1 and 1.2 add up to 1.6, it is because combined vector force is a squared equation.

This is why lower-acceleration cars have a faster, earlier apex; because less of the grip can be used to accelerate the car down the track during the exit so it can be used to increase corner entry and apex speed. This creates the best net force during corner exit for that type of car.

In all corner exit situations though, the driver's goal is the same. To generate as much force as possible to push them down the track in the ideal direction. However, as odd as it may seem, in most cars you are actually generating more acceleration force down the track early in the corner exit when you are more sideways than when you are close to going straight at the end. This has an influence on how you optimally drive different cars at corner exit. Now let's continue on to our next (bad) corner entry technique.

THE SUPER-LATE APEX MYTH REVISITED

Introduced earlier in the corner exit section we are now getting back to the super-late apex for a more in-depth look. This time however, we are using the optimized spiral entry we've learned instead of the original circular one. Now that we understand how the Euler spiral works, we can apply that understanding to what is actually happening with a super-late apex.

Let's just go ahead and lay down an illustration so we can work through it. We've put the darker super-late apex line over a white optimal line to more clearly see the difference. We've also used a car with some good acceleration potential at corner exit. The whole purpose of this technique is to start accelerating earlier to maximize corner exit speed so we definitely need to at least start with a car that is able to make use of this. For the super-late apex line, what we see is the car's entry spiral meeting its acceleration arc out in the middle of the track at the point we labeled false apex. Although not displayed, the tire forces would basically all be going in the proper direction so that would be correct and not an issue. You can also see how the final apex radius is bigger, and therefore, the exit speed higher in the super-late apex car. That seems to be a good thing and working as intended. So where is the problem?

Again, it all comes back to the nature of what the spiral represents and that is the absolute fastest way to get the car to change direction. In the super-late apex car, the minimum speed at the false apex is going to be slower than the optimized car's apex because of the tighter radius. Plus it's going to take longer to even get to the minimum speed at the false apex than the optimized apex.

Remember, the spiral represents the fastest way to change direction so if you start your spiral later, as you must in the super-late apex car, you are by definition unable to get your turning done as quickly. The optimized car will actually get to its apex and begin accelerating before the super-late apex car has even reached its minimum speed at its false apex.

Again, the super-late apex car is basically optimizing the corner for an obstruction out at the false apex that is not really there. Understanding this idea of how the apex should always be some sort of obstruction is actually a quick way you can check your cornering. If your minimum corner speed is not at the point that is actually hindering you from going faster through the corner, then you have made a mistake and need to adjust your corner entry.

So the ultimate problem with the super-late apex goes back again to the fact that you want to begin accelerating again as quickly as possible based on time, not distance. We can clearly see that although we would have a faster straightaway speed, overall this is going to be a slower way of taking the corner. As mentioned earlier with the qualifying run approach, there will be a time and place for this technique and being able to know when and how to break the rules all comes back to having a good understanding of what we are trying to accomplish in a corner and make intelligent decisions on how Line Theory can be applied.

ADVANCED CORNER ENTRY CONSIDERATIONS

So far we have only looked at a traditional corner that starts with threshold braking and has no unique considerations, but of course racetracks are not only comprised of these standard corners and so we must learn how to apply what we've learned to more advanced situations.

> Knowing the optimal technique and having the perfect corner in your head, even if you aren't able to do it yet, gives you something to work toward and eventually an advantage.

We know we need to do an Euler spiral entry when we start with threshold braking, but what happens when we don't need to brake as much? Many high-speed corners or corners after a very short straight won't require straight line threshold braking. The solution is actually quite simple, but sometimes not intuitive and can be quite difficult from a car control standpoint to do properly. Let's look at the same corner at Laguna Seca as before, but this time we are lowering our entry speed so threshold braking won't be required and see what happens.

FULL THROTTLE INTO THE SPIRAL

We've now added a white line coming from the straight and going into the beginning of the spiral. The white line represents the car is at full throttle. As you can see, when dealing with a corner situation like this you will still use the spiral, but you start the deceleration portion after you have already entered.

In the former example you might be starting the spiral at 60 mph after threshold braking, but now let's say full power from the last corner only brought you to 50 mph at that same point. If you started turning as hard as you could right away, your spiral would be too small and you would run off the inside of the track. If you drove further before starting the spiral, you would hit the apex too late for an optimal corner exit.

Full throttle ends

The shape of the track at corner exit always determines the optimal apex and therefore spiral. The speed you carry from the previous corner only affects the point you start decelerating. This could be a standard braking point before the spiral or it could be a point in the spiral itself.

So in this example, you would actually use the same optimal spiral from before since it's the same corner exit, but this time you would enter it at full speed. Then when your speed matched the attainable speed for that point in the spiral, you would switch to trail braking and begin turning as quickly as possible. Let's say in this example that would be at 53 mph, which would be fairly soon after entering the spiral. As mentioned earlier, this sudden switchover can be quite hard to do from a car control standpoint because going from a full throttle turn-in straight to turning and braking is not easy to do properly.

Even a more advanced driver might choose to just use lighter braking through the entire spiral rather than turning in at full throttle and switching at the last instant. The improvement in lap time would be minimal compared to the risk of messing up and blowing the corner. Only a very confident and skilled driver might attempt to do this in a race situation.

This is a great example though, of how knowing the optimal technique and having the perfect corner in your head, even if you aren't able to do it yet, gives you something to work toward and eventually an advantage. While your competitors might brake earlier or do a more circular entry in the corner because it's easier and they don't know they are losing time, the knowledgeable driver can keep pushing their skills to find that last little bit.

Before we move on, a key thing to note here is that you will not truly be on the limit when entering the spiral at full throttle although you will be very near it. If you turn into a corner truly on the limit without deceleration, it means you have a circular entry path and are losing time. Notice that we say deceleration though. So far, we have always referred to driving an Euler spiral shaped entry as braking and turning, but it's important to understand that the spiral does not always just mean trail braking, as we'll see now.

BRAKING OR DECELERATION?

Let's look at a more extreme example where the speed loss required for the corner is low enough that you would be entering the spiral very close to the optimum apex speed. This is what many high-speed corners will look like in lower-powered cars, but it could be any corner if it's preceded by a short enough straight. Let's change corners so we can use a more realistic example. Staying with Laguna Seca, let's go to turn 6 which is a high-speed corner and many cars won't need to lose much speed here.

Full throttle ends

This time, the driver carries full throttle almost all the way to the apex before he enters the deceleration phase of the spiral and begins turning as quickly as possible. He then goes right back to maximum acceleration at the apex. You might be thinking that it's not very realistic to go from full throttle to brakes back to full throttle in such a small amount of time and you'd be absolutely correct.

> Your real world technique is going to be determined by the vehicle, your car control abilities, and the compromises they may require from what the theoretical optimum is.

While the spiral does represent the fastest way to change direction and usually that means trail braking, in certain situations you lose too much grip efficiency by doing quick load transitions that you are better off not doing the theoretical optimum. In this example, for instance, if you got hard on the brakes right when you theoretically should, you would most likely not even have gotten the load to transfer and maximize your deceleration by the time you even hit the apex. Not to mention being able to get back to full throttle by then. If you had a car that transferred load instantaneously and was driven by a robot you might actually do the theoretical optimum, but in reality, this deceleration phase is going to most likely just be a lift of the throttle. Maybe not even a full lift. It could be just a partial lift. Even with a partial lift, you are still going to be decelerating from tire and air drag forces.

Therefore, your real world technique is going to be determined by the vehicle, your car control abilities, and the compromises they may require from what the theoretical optimum is. The goal is still the same, which is to turn as quickly as possible, but it's up to the driver to determine how much they can get away with and still make it to maximum acceleration at the apex.

Also, as in the previous example, in the first full throttle phase you shouldn't be truly on the limit. Again, if you turn in at full throttle and are truly on the limit, but have to lift to make the apex, it means you can start your spiral a little bit sooner. If you turn in under full throttle while truly at the limit and don't have to lift to make the apex then guess what? This is no longer technically a corner. It's just a curved straightaway and you don't need Line Theory anymore.

We've gone over a few examples now of applying Line Theory rules to more advanced situations and introduced the real world considerations and compromises you will have to deal with. Let's take a step back now and look at what we've learned, but from the driver's-eye view. Up until now we've looked at a lot of ideas and hopefully you have begun to grasp the fundamental rules of Line Theory, but as we begin to wrap up let's see if you can begin to picture what this will all look like once you are in the cockpit.

Karting is not just for kids. With cornering forces in excess of 2 g, true racing karts are serious machines and very few other vehicles can rival them in terms of performance.

THE DRIVER'S-EYE VIEW

We want you to remember that the primary goal of learning Line Theory is that it allows you to picture a perfect lap in your mind and remove that doubt many drivers feel over what they should be doing. So far, we've talked a lot about the optimum and perfect way to drive a corner, but one of the first things to understand when trying to start applying these rules in the real world is that you are going to make mistakes. Even after years of training, you will still make mistakes. We are human after all.

Making mistakes is okay and making constant mistakes is actually required to drive at the limit. Your main goal is to try to make smaller and smaller mistakes and catch them sooner. For a novice, a mistake might be a spin or driving off track. As you gain experience and master these techniques, a mistake could become having to make a slight steering correction at corner entry that a novice wouldn't see or even realize was a mistake. Eventually, with enough training, you will be able to do track-record level laps, but still know where you are losing that last little bit of time. If you ever think you have actually achieved a truly perfect corner, you just haven't made it to that next level of car control yet.

This section also begins to blur the line between Line Theory and car control. As mentioned earlier, Line Theory rules assume you are driving at the limit and although there are big similarities between driving different vehicles at the limit, some will require more specialized car control techniques. Car control, in essence, is about managing inputs and outputs. The outputs are your controls over the vehicle. Primarily brakes, throttle, and steering. The inputs would be all the information you are getting from the car and your surroundings. Visual, audio, tactile, etc... We call these inputs cues.

Car control is a huge topic of its own and in a further title we will be covering all these cues in depth and you'll learn how they vary in the precision of information they provide. You'll learn which cues you should pay attention to and which you should mostly ignore. But for this driver's eye section, there is one cue that we will cover, because it is essentially the real world representation of the core goal of Line Theory. The goal of maximizing and directing force and how it affects your movement. This is ultimately the primary cue that you will learn to use. If you can develop your sensitivity to this cue, you will be able to apply it to virtually any vehicle. From karting, off-road, and even motorcycles or practically any other vehicle you can think of. Once you adapt to the controls needed you will be able to start turning fast laps anywhere. We call this fundamental representation of Line Theory...

The Universal Cue.

THE UNIVERSAL CUE

For many people, it helps when you realize that the core goal of Line Theory and the Universal Cue are actually quite intuitive. Let's do a fun little thought experiment so you can see how you are actually already preprogrammed to pay attention to force and movement. You just might not realize it yet or understand how to apply it on track.

Everything you do to control a car should ultimately be in service of moving you in the ideal direction by maximizing the force pushing you that way.

Imagine you are driving down an abandoned post-apocalyptic highway when some cannibal marauders appear over the horizon heading your way. Since you are not too fond of the idea of becoming somebody's lunch you know that a hasty retreat is probably your best option. So what do you do? What is the thought process that would go through your head in that situation? Would you think, "Okay, I'll smoothly apply the brakes and turn in and then unwind the steering wheel while feeding in the throttle?" Probably not. You would probably just be thinking. "Let's get the hell out of here!" Your brain would be screaming at you to turn around and every single movement you made with the controls would be your best efforts in trying to go back the way you came as fast as possible.

Even though you might not realize it, you would be trying to maximize and direct those forces that turn you around as quickly as possible. Remember, just like we learned from the section on the Euler spiral, maximizing these forces is what causes our path to change direction and move us in the ideal direction as quickly as possible. Being able to accurately sense the changes in overall movement of the car is the Universal Cue.

At any instant, you would effectively be asking yourself, does turning the steering, pushing the brakes, or using throttle move the car in the ideal direction more? If the answer is yes, then it is the right thing to do. If the answer is no, then it is the wrong thing to do.

Everything you do to control a car should ultimately be in service of moving you in the ideal direction by maximizing the force pushing you that way. Line Theory teaches you in what direction that force should be heading and the Universal Cue gives you the feedback you need to tell the car what to do to get it done.

Be warned though. It's doubtful many drivers will be able to use this cue in isolation, especially at the beginning. While we hope you get the basic idea of what it should feel like from the marauders example, there would clearly be a difference in how fast an expert and novice driver would be able to complete that turnaround. Many quick "seat of the pants" drivers who are very fast right away are naturally very good at following this cue. Just about every driver already uses it to a certain extent though, even if they don't realize it. But if a driver understands what it is, even if they aren't able to fully use it yet, they will be better off in the end as the Universal Cue simply represents the basic physics at work in a corner.

Let's run through a few quick examples so we can see how the Universal Cue is applied and how it differentiates from the other car control cues that we call secondary cues. During threshold braking it's generally considered bad to lock up the tires. Other than causing flatspotting, it causes grip loss and removes the ability to steer. The secondary cues here would be hearing the tire squeal, seeing smoke, or in an open-wheel car, actually seeing the tire stop rotating. But the Universal Cue would only be concerned with how that lockup changed the direction or amount of force pushing you back the way you came. That change in force is really all that matters from a Line Theory standpoint. Since you are straight-line threshold braking the ideal direction you want to maximize force in would be straight behind you. A driver that had trained themselves to pay attention to the Universal Cue would be able to see and feel how that tire lockup was making the car receive less force in the proper direction and was decelerating slower than it had been prior to lockup.

The Universal Cue is the final cue that offers the most precise answer for what you should be doing. It might be helpful to think of using all the secondary cues as getting you in the ballpark and then the Universal Cue is that last layer that provides ultimate speed. Sometimes the secondary cues might give conflicting information or simply information that is not precise enough. The Universal Cue will always provide the correct answer, but only if you are sensitive enough to recognize it.

> The Universal Cue will always provide the correct answer, but only if you are sensitive enough to recognize it.

Let's look at another example of how this works in a different part of the corner. Let's say we are now heading past the apex and the ideal direction would be sideways from our current direction of travel. If the car began to spin out from too much power applied, the secondary cues might be hearing the revs climb too fast from wheelspin or noticing the car rotating too much. But the Universal Cue would again only be concerned with whether or not the actions you just performed changed the rate at which the car moved toward the ideal direction.

It's important to realize that it's actually the center of gravity of the car that you are trying to move, not the front tires as might at first feel more intuitive. Remember again, the actual rotation of the car doesn't matter. Although it is important as a secondary cue, which way the car is facing has no bearing on Line Theory and the Universal Cue. An easy way to apply this is to focus on getting you, the driver, to go in the direction the ideal forces should be pushing you. The driver is usually situated very closely to the center of gravity of the car so it's helpful to retrain your brain into thinking in this context.

Of course, using the Universal Cue on an empty highway is one thing. Turning around as quickly as possible is easier if it doesn't matter where exactly your path takes you. But if you wish to be able to use it effectively on a racetrack, you must be able to visualize the entire corner and its limits as you drive through it. Not only where you are in the corner, but also which direction your center of gravity is moving at any instant. You'll need a running picture in your mind, almost as if you are viewing the corner from above, using tire forces to push your racecar around as if it's a game piece. Once a driver's car control abilities rise to the level of basically becoming automatic, then all that remains is the Universal Cue and how every action affects which way the car moves. It's no small wonder why top drivers have amazing spatial awareness abilities.

As we wrap up, we'll give you a homework assignment so you can start to get your head around this concept of the Universal Cue. Watch some onboard laps of drivers and while using your newfound knowledge of Line Theory, try to visualize which way the forces should ideally be pushing the car as the driver navigates the course. This will allow you to try and start picking up on this cue without having to worry about dealing with the extra mental energy controlling the car yourself requires. Try to visualize the course from overhead and how the car's center of gravity is being moved around and accelerated in different directions. It's helpful to look at only the track. Don't watch the steering wheel. Try turning off the sound so the only cue you can pick up on is the movement of the car on track.

Watch laps from fast drivers and slow drivers. See if you can spot how the fast drivers move the car's center of gravity in the proper direction more effectively. Find a lap where a driver makes a bobble and has to correct. See if you can spot how this affected the car's center of gravity and reduced its movement in the proper direction.

We're not going to lie. This is quite hard for many people to start visualizing a racecar's movement in this way. But once you can, and your car control level reaches the point that you can start applying it effectively, you'll be amazed at the laps it produces because you'll simply be following the same basic physics the astronaut was. If you follow the laws of physics, you can't go wrong. All the complexities of controlling the car become secondary. You could look at telemetry data and see picture perfect steering, brake, and throttle traces, but it would not be from any preplanned strategy. Those perfect inputs are all just from following the basic physics at work and the Universal Cue. You aren't driving a car anymore. You are just moving your game piece.

Watching onboard videos can be a great way to start training yourself to pick up on The Universal Cue.

BONUS SECTION: ADVANCED RACING PHYSICS

We wanted to add this bonus section at the end for those looking for a little more in depth analysis. This is all still pretty basic, but if you always struggled with math, you can safely skim through this section without worrying about digesting all of it right now, as it doesn't include any new rules. It might be something you refer back to later as you look for a deeper understanding.

Now that we've looked at the principles of Line Theory, let's take a more advanced look at the physics involved because it can really help as you try to put the Universal Cue into practice on track. We've learned that the Euler spiral is the shape of a path that has a continuously decreasing radius. Another way to understand this is that it's simply made of a series of smaller and smaller circles. As you enter a spiral, the first circle has an infinite radius and then the circles will get progressively smaller and smaller until you reach whatever apex you need to reach.

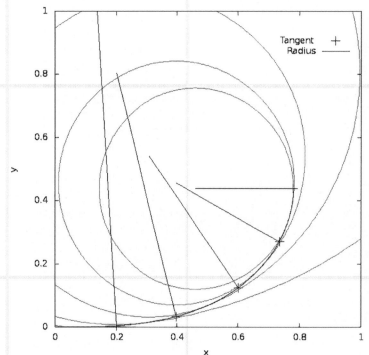

This illustration shows just a few of the circles, but there are an infinite number and it's the driver's goal to get to that next smaller circle as quickly as possible. As we've learned, this is accomplished by combining steering and braking to generate the maximum force possible in the optimum direction.

Let's now use this to look at our forces in a few places during our corner entry. We're going to assume for our example that the car generates the same force in all directions. In reality, the grip will always be variable from all kinds of different factors, but it's generally going to be pretty even in most cars, at least at corner entry.

At the very beginning of the spiral, the car will be right at the end of full threshold braking mode with maximum longitudinal force pushing it directly backwards. Technically, this is toward a point an infinite distance away.

Let's now fast forward to the apex. We are now in pure cornering mode with maximum lateral acceleration and minimal longitudinal acceleration. At this one instant, we are actually traveling on a circular path at whatever radius we achieved at the apex. Our primary force is pushing us toward the center of the circle we are currently on. You can see in this illustration that this is still pushing us in the same direction as the forces from our pure braking right as we entered the spiral. Straight backwards down the track.

Now let's look at a point in the middle of the spiral. At our halfway point, we have a combination of forces where about half our tire forces are going toward braking and half are going toward steering. From a physics standpoint, our steering forces are pushing us laterally toward the center of the big white circle the car is currently on and our braking forces are pushing us directly backwards on a tangent to our current direction decelerating the car. These tangent forces are actually called the Euler force named after the same mathematician that originated the Euler spiral.

Remember though, tire forces are not really separate. A tire generates one force in one direction. So if we use some basic math we find that our forces are creating a combined vector force, you guessed it, pushing us almost directly backwards down the track. But actually now, not quite directly backwards...

While in general we want to generate the maximum force we can pushing us backwards at the same angle as the track, some force is needed to move us over toward the apex and rotate the car. When we started our spiral, the force was pushing us directly backwards, infinitely far away, and when we reach the apex it is pushing us toward the center of the circle we are currently on. In this ideal spiral, the direction of force needing to be maximized will steadily progress from one point to the other as the car moves along the spiral.

Now don't be intimidated by this, you don't need to start doing trigonometry on track to figure out what you should do. Because of the varying nature of grip and car capabilities, our spiral will not be perfect and the actual direction of force you are trying to maximize will be constantly changing at any given time. Plus, every little correction by the driver will also redirect the forces somewhat and so the driver will constantly be making small updates to their spiral to optimize their acceleration in the ideal direction while also trying to arrive at the apex at the perfect speed. In general though, a driver will want to concentrate on pushing the car toward the ideal direction as quickly as possible. If this causes you to arrive at the apex at the perfect speed to give you an ideal corner exit, you know you've optimized the corner. Optimized for your current skill level anyway. Also remember, maximizing force in the perfect direction will also cause the car to reduce its radius as quickly as possible and this gives you another form of feedback that you are doing it correctly.

DRIVING THE GRAPH

We also wanted to offer one last way of looking at a corner. A very useful way to picture the Universal Cue is to look at the movement through a corner on an X/Y graph.

This illustration shows the astronaut doing a full 180-degree corner. Their speed at the beginning of their spiral will be 100 mph and they drop to 30 mph at the apex and then back up to 100 mph. If we consider their speed on each axis separately, that means that in the same time their speed goes from 100 to zero on the X-axis, their speed on the Y-axis goes from zero up to 30. As the spiral starts, they are being pushed straight back toward the ship, and right at the apex they are also being pushed directly toward the ship.

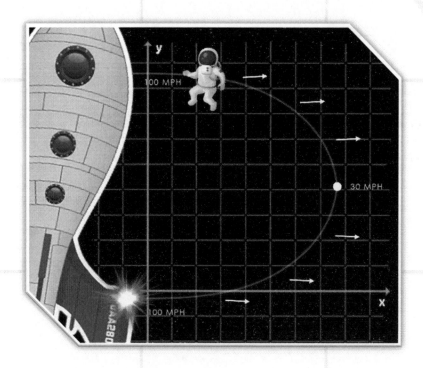

In between these two sections they need to give enough force with their extinguisher along the Y axis to go from zero to 30 mph, but then back down to zero after the apex. While it takes a good bit less force to go from 0-30 then it does to go 100-0, it does require some. For a car, it's not just the shape of the corner, but also the rotation of the vehicle that will cause this to be necessary. Unlike the astronaut, a car can't turn in place and actually must change its path in order to provide force in a new direction.

> The goal of the driver should be to maximize their force on the X-axis while using the minimum force necessary to move them along the Y-axis.

This visualizing of the path on an X/Y graph is not just academic, the goal of the driver should be to maximize their force on the X-axis while using the minimum force necessary to move them along the Y-axis. Being able to visualize the car's movement and change in speed on its different X/Y axis can help a driver maximize and direct forces through the corner.

THE FINAL CORNER

It is our sincere hope that this book has helped to point you in the right direction, the ideal direction. You rarely see a happier face than one of a new driver at their first event. The ear-to-ear grin that comes with the simple pleasure of pushing a vehicle to its limits. We really hate to see that face turn to a scowl once the pursuit for an ever-lower lap time rears its fearsome head. The pursuit that sends many frustrated racers down countless dead ends in search of speed. But once you have completely digested and integrated the concepts taught in this book, we promise that simple pleasure of driving will return.

Eventually you will no longer see every corner as a completely separate puzzle with a unique answer. Once you truly begin to understand, you will see Line Theory fundamentals in every corner, in every car. Confusion will turn to confidence. The amazing fast laps you used to marvel at will turn into achievable goals. You just have to remember to always ask yourself…

"What would the astronaut do?"

GLOSSARY OF MOTORSPORT TERMS

ACKERMAN STEERING

A steering geometry design that allows the toe angle of the front tires to change dynamically as the steering wheel turns with the standard setup being an increase in negative toe with an increase in steering. This was originally developed to minimize tire scrub as during a turn the inner and outer tire must travel on different size circles, but variations on the basic principle have been used in motorsport in an attempt to increase performance. This is rarely directly adjustable on most cars and is primarily a consideration during the design phase, but many karts allow easy adjustments of Ackerman steering.

ALIGNMENT

Adjusting a vehicles suspension to alter how the tires are situated in relation to the chassis and each other. The primary adjustments being camber, caster, toe. These settings can be adjusted to improve performance, tire wear, and alter handling characteristics.

ANTI-ROLL BAR

Anti-roll bars are part of a car's suspension system. They are sometimes also called anti-sway bars or stabilizer bars. Due to the way they are designed and mounted, unlike the primary suspension springs they increase a car's stiffness in roll, but not in ride. They are generally designed to be a relatively easy adjustment to make and are typically the primary way to adjust a car's balance. Some more advanced racecars even have cockpit adjustable anti-roll bars.

APEX

In basic terms the apex is the point on the inside portion of a corner that a car passes closest too.

AUTOCROSS

Autocross (also called "Gymkhana," "Solo", "Auto-x" or "Autoslalom") is a timed competition in which drivers navigate through a defined course typically marked by cones in a large open paved area. Autocross differs from road racing and oval racing in that generally there is only one car on the track, racing against the clock rather than directly with other cars.

BALANCE

Car balance describes the tendency of a car either toward oversteer or understeer. For example, a normal street car would be described as having a balance that is more biased toward understeer.

BRAKE BIAS

Indicated as a percentage. This indicates the relative amount of brake pressure applied to the front brakes. E.g. 52% would indicate that the front brakes were receiving 52% of the brake pressure and the rear brakes would be receiving 48%. Brake bias is often adjustable from the cockpit in many racecars and is generally used to maximize braking potential and control vehicle balance while using the brakes.

BUMPSTEER

Bump steer or roll steer is the term for the tendency of the tires of a car to steer by themselves as the suspension travels through its range of motion. This is generally seen as a negative and minimizing any bump steer is typically seen as ideal.

BUMP STOP

Also known as bump rubbers, these are typically cone shaped polyurethane parts placed on the damper that prevent the suspension from compressing too far and becoming damaged.

CAMBER

The camber angle identifies how far the tire slants away from vertical when viewed directly from the front or back of the vehicle. Camber is expressed in degrees, and is said to be negative when the top of the tire tilts inward toward the center of the vehicle and positive when the top leans away from the center of the vehicle.

CAMBER GAIN

Camber gain is the difference of the camber angle after a certain amount of suspension travel. This is usually defined based on 1" of suspension compression. For example if static camber is -3 degrees and goes to -4.5 degrees at 1" compression, it has -1.5 degree camber gain.

CAMBER THRUST

When a wheel has some amount of camber, the deflection in the tire makes it acts like a cone rolling across the ground and creates a force in the direction the tire is leaned.

CAR CONTROL

The ability of a driver to control a car at the limits of the tires and car performance.

CASTER

The caster angle identifies the forward or backward slope of a line drawn through the upper and lower steering pivot points when viewed directly from the side of the vehicle. Caster is expressed in degrees and is measured by comparing a line running through the steering system's upper and lower pivot points to a line drawn perpendicular to the ground. Caster is said to be positive if the line slopes towards the rear of the vehicle at the top, and negative if the line slopes towards the front.

CENTER OF GRAVITY (CG)

The center of gravity is a geometric property of any object. The center of gravity is the average location of the weight of an object. For a vehicle, this is the point from which all forces created at the tires react too. It can be described as a certain point in the vehicle on an X, Y, and Z coordinate. If you suspended a vehicle from this point, it would rotate in all directions freely.

CHICANE

A chicane is a section of a racetrack where one turn is quickly followed by another in the opposite direction. This can also sometimes be described as a compromise corner or esses.

CONTACT PATCH

The contact patch is the portion of a vehicle's tire that is in actual contact with the road surface.

CORNER WEIGHT

The practice of adjusting a vehicle's suspension to distribute the weight among the tires. The ideal can differ based on goals whether it be even loading or increased load on two tires and less on the other two. This is also known as cross weight, or wedge.

CURB

A feature at the edge of a racetrack typically placed near expected apexes and other high travel areas. They are generally designed to compromise handling in comparison to the normal racing surface. There are many designs possible, but they are usually brightly painted in alternating colors.

DAMPER

A part of a car's suspension designed to reduce oscillations and modify the dynamic movement of the car. Also known as a shock absorber.

DOWNFORCE

Downforce is a downwards thrust created by the aerodynamic characteristics of a car. The purpose of downforce is to allow a car to travel faster through a corner by increasing the vertical force on the tires, thus creating more grip.

DRAFTING

Drafting or slipstreaming is a technique where two or more vehicles follow each other closely reducing the overall effect of drag due to exploiting the lead car's slipstream.

FLAT SPOT

If a car tire locks up excessively under braking and stops spinning it will wear a flat area on a portion of the tread. The flat spot can then often be felt as a vibration of the tire as it rolls.

HAIRPIN

A hairpin turn, named for its resemblance to a hairpin/bobby pin, is a bend in a road with a very acute inner angle, making it necessary for an oncoming vehicle to turn 180°.

KARTING

Kart racing or karting is a variant of open-wheel motorsport with small, open, four-wheeled vehicles called karts, go-karts, or gearbox/shifter karts depending on the design. They are usually raced on scaled-down circuits. Karting is commonly perceived as the stepping-stone to the higher ranks of motorsport.

LIMIT (THE)

The maximum speed a car can attain while turning before a car begins to either oversteer or understeer excessively.

MECHANICAL TRAIL

Mechanical trail is the perpendicular distance between the steering axis and the point of contact between the front tire and the ground. Past the design process, the amount can typically only be modified by altering caster. An increase in caster will increase mechanical trail, which increases the force trying to center the steering wheel. This felt force increase comes from the greater distance between the steering axis and the contact patch causing a greater torque on the steering system. So although the force felt at the steering wheel is greater, the force at the tire remains the same.

OVERSTEER

In the simplest terms, this is when the rear tires exceed their limit before the front tires while negotiating a turn. This is an unstable condition that can lead to a spin.

PITCH

The forward and backward rotating motion along the length of a car. Deceleration will generally cause a car to pitch forward whereas acceleration will cause it to pitch backwards.

PNEUMATIC TRAIL

Pneumatic trail is caused by the progressive build-up of lateral force along the length of the contact patch, such that lateral forces are greater towards the rear of the contact patch and this creates a torque on the tire called the self-aligning torque. For most tires, pneumatic trail will increase as the tire approaches its peak traction and thus increase steering force, but prior to actually reaching the peak the pneumatic trail will reduce due to sliding at the rear of the contact patch. Pneumatic trail is primarily important because of its effect on steering forces. Together with mechanical trail, they are called total trail.

PYROMETER (TIRE)

A tool used to measure temperature. For racing, this is typically used to measure the temperature of the tire tread by using a probe style pyrometer and inserting the probe directly into the surface of the tire. A common practice is to take the measurement across the face of the tire in three different places from the inside, middle, and outside.

RAKE

Rake refers to the angle that the body of a car has in relation to the ground. It is typically measured as the distance from the lowest point on the body to the ground at the front and rear of the car. Positive rake is when the rear of the car is higher in the front. Negative rake is when the front of the car is higher than the rear. It is primarily important for aerodynamic reasons.

RIDE

Also known as heave, this is the up/down movement of the entire chassis of a car in response to its movement on track or the suspension geometry reacting to tire forces. It is defined as up/down movement of the center of gravity of the chassis in relation to the tires.

RIDE HEIGHT

This is the static or dynamic measure of a car chassis in relation to the ground. It is usually measured from the lowest points on the car that will make contact with the ground first if the ride height is too low.

ROLL

The side-to-side rotating motion along the width of a car. Cornering forces will generally cause a car to roll in the opposite direction of the turn.

ROLL CENTER

There are many varying ways that engineers define a roll center, but essentially, it is a result of the suspension geometry that alters handling in a similar fashion to adjusting anti-roll bars. A higher roll center at one end of the car will increase roll resistance there and vice-a-versa.

SCRUB RADIUS

The scrub radius is the distance in front view between the steering axis and the center of the contact patch of the wheel, where both would theoretically touch the road. If the steering axis intersection point is outboard of the center of the contact patch it is negative, if inside the contact patch it is positive.

SECTOR

Used in lap timing, a sector is any timed portion of a lap. Many times, there will be 3-5 official sectors designated for a track, but for setup/training purposes, a driver and team can set custom sectors using their own telemetry system.

SIM RACING

Sim (simulated) racing is the collective term for computer software (i.e. a vehicle simulation game) that attempts to accurately simulate auto racing (a racing video game), complete with real-world variables such as fuel usage, damage, tire wear and grip, and suspension settings. This can range from console-based games using a gamepad to advanced full motion simulators.

SKIDPAD

A skidpad or skidpan is a circular area of flat pavement used for various tests of a car's handling. The most common skidpad use is testing lateral acceleration, measured in g. Some racetracks have dedicated skidpads, but any flat pavement of sufficient size can be used.

SLICK

A racing slick (also known as a "slick tire") is a type of tire that has a smooth tread used mostly in auto racing. By eliminating any grooves cut into the tread, such tires provide the largest possible contact patch to the road, and maximize traction for any given tire dimension in dry conditions. Grooved tire tread only offers a grip advantage in wet or loose (gravel, dirt, snow) conditions.

SLIP ANGLE

Slip angle or sideslip angle is the angle between a rolling wheel's actual direction of travel and the direction towards which it is pointing. All tires experience slip angle while turning because of the tire distorting with a "peak" slip angle achieved at maximum cornering force. Because of slip angle at the rear tires, a car will have a sideways attitude to the direction of travel while cornering at speed even if the tire is not sliding across the track.

SLIP RATIO

The wheel speed divided by the actual speed of the vehicle. We can also measure the slip ratio as a percentage. E.g. a slip percentage of 10% means the tire is moving 10% faster/slower than the road surface. One important thing to remember is that the slip ratio is not the same as wheel spin. When acceleration/braking torque is applied to a tire the tire distorts and moves along the road without actually slipping, so a wheel can be moving faster/slower than the road without any wheel spin.

STEADY STATE HANDLING

Steady state handling refers to the handling characteristics of a car that is not currently undergoing rapid change. Examples of this could be cornering at the limit or threshold braking. This is as opposed to transient handling.

TELEMETRY

Telemetry (or data acquisition) is the practice of collecting information during a test or race and using it to properly tune the car for optimum performance. Examples of measurements on a racecar include accelerations (G forces) in three axes, temperature readings, wheel speed, and suspension displacement

TOE

The toe angle identifies the exact direction the tires are pointed compared to the centerline of the vehicle when viewed from directly above. Toe is expressed in either degrees or fractions-of-an-inch, and an axle is said to have positive toe-in when imaginary lines running through the centerlines of the tires intersect in front of the vehicle and have negative toe-out when they diverge.

TRANSIENT HANDLING

Transient handling refers to the handling characteristics of a car that is experiencing rapid change. An example of this could be the fast transition from one direction to the other in the middle of a chicane or a driver having to make a quick correction to avoid a spin. This is as opposed to steady-state handling.

UNDERSTEER

In the simplest terms, this is when the front tires exceed their limit before the rear tires while negotiating a turn. This is a stable condition as opposed to oversteer.

WHEELSPIN

When a tire begins to spin too fast because of excess power applied. This causes a reduction in acceleration.

YAW

The rotation of a car as if it is turning left or right Yaw defines any movement on this axis. A car spinning straight down an icy road would be changing yaw even though it would be moving in one direction as it spins.

Other Motorsport Education Titles by
PARADIGM SHIFT DRIVER DEVELOPMENT

PERFECT CONTROL

Do you understand the true meaning of driving at the limit? Learn how to identify and prioritize the different visual, auditory, and tactile car control cues, plus the optimal driver inputs needed to extract %100 from practically any vehicle. We will also look in-depth at the Universal Cue. The driving cue that directly represents the physics of racing and provides the final layer of car control precision. Learn how world-class drivers use it to self-evaluate and perfect their on track performance.

THE PERFECT CORNER 2

Ready for the next level? Learn how the physics of racing can be applied to advanced track sections. We show you the rules needed to optimize double apexes, chicanes, and even how the Double Apex Rule can be used to ideally correct mistakes in your line as you drive. The final section will really put you to the test as we break down some of the most complicated corner sequences in the world. You'll see how there is no such thing as a throwaway corner and how every single section of a track can be driven to perfection.

These titles are available wherever quality books are sold or by visiting us at www.paradigmshiftracing.com

Printed in Great Britain
by Amazon